BRICKS AND CONCRETE

This volume is part of a series offering home owners detailed instructions on repairs, construction and improvements which they can undertake themselves.

HOME REPAIR
AND IMPROVEMENT

BRICKS AND CONCRETE

BY THE EDITORS OF
TIME-LIFE BOOKS

TIME-LIFE BOOKS
AMSTERDAM

TIME-LIFE BOOKS

EUROPEAN EDITOR: Kit van Tulleken
Design Director: Ed Skyner
Photography Director: Pamela Marke
Chief of Research: Vanessa Kramer
Chief Sub-Editor: Ilse Gray

HOME REPAIR AND IMPROVEMENT

EDITORIAL STAFF FOR BRICKS AND CONCRETE
Editor: William Frankel
Assistant Editor: Edward Brash
Picture Editor: Rhea Finkelstein
Designer: Herbert H. Quarmby
Associate Designer: Robert McKee
Staff Writers: Marian Gordon Goldman, Angela D.
Goodman, Simone D. Gossner, Lee Greene, Lee Hassig,
Michael Luftman, Don Nelson, Sandra Streepey,
Rosalind Stubenberg, Reiko Uyeshima
Art Associates: Faye Eng, Kaye Sherry Hirsh, Richard
Salcer, Victoria Vebell, Mary Wilshire
Editorial Assistant: Eleanor G. Kask

EUROPEAN EDITION
Editor: Gillian Moore
Head Researcher: Jackie Matthews
Text Editor: Tony Allan
Researcher: Judy Perle
Designers: Michael Morey, Paul Reeves
Sub-Editor: Sally Rowland
Editorial Assistant: Rebecca Smith

EDITORIAL PRODUCTION
Chief: Ellen Brush
Production Assistants: Stephanie Lee, Jane Lillicrap,
Linda Mallett
Art Department: Janet Matthew
Editorial Department: Theresa John, Debra Lelliott

THE CONSULTANTS: Dave Beadle worked for over 15 years as a technical
writer for the Cement and Concrete Association. He is the author of many
articles and booklets on building and civil engineering, and is currently
an independent writer and consultant.

L.I. Pursehouse has over 30 years' practical experience of the building
trade. He is a member of the Master Builders Association of New South
Wales, Australia.

Lelland L. Gallup is a former Assistant Professor of Housing and Design
at New York State College of Human Ecology, Cornell University,
Ithaca, New York. He is responsible for a series of innovative home
maintenance courses given to home owners and home associations.

Contents

Materials of Lasting Beauty

Building for keeps. A bricklayer shapes mortar with a jointing tool to put the finishing touch to a wall. The wall's rugged beauty—like that of all paving and structures that are made of bricks and concrete—should last for generations without needing any further attention.

For transforming a garden into an outdoor living space, masonry and paving have no equals. A brick or a stone wall, a flight of concrete steps, a tiled patio, or a path made of paving slabs—all are beautiful, durable and relatively inexpensive. Well-designed walls and paving can enhance every sort of setting. Bricks, blocks and tiles are available in more colours, textures, shapes and sizes than any other kind of building material; freshly mixed concrete can be formed and then finished to suit almost any design and dimensions you can imagine. And while natural quarry stone is often an expensive purchase, bricks, blocks, tiles and paving slabs are obtainable in a wide range of prices. Concrete, the most adaptable of all, is widely considered to be the world's lowest-cost building material.

The most important consideration, however, is that bricks, stone and concrete are permanent. The materials require little, if any, maintenance to stay in perfect condition once they have been installed, and they are easy to repair or restore if they do suffer damage. They are fireproof and rustproof, and they are more resistant to traffic, sun, salt, pests and air pollutants than most substances—including their major rivals, wood and metal.

Masonry structures and paving are exceptionally strong, capable of bearing the great weight that presses inwards on them. Although they are not so sturdy against stresses that tend to bend or stretch them, this weakness can be easily remedied by metal reinforcement, which minimizes cracking in large concrete slabs such as drives or patios. Lightweight footings, specially designed to hold low walls or barbecue fireplaces, do not usually require any reinforcing.

The only major enemies these materials have are unstable ground and frost. In most cases, both unstable foundation soils and also the risk of frost heave in cold climates can be overcome simply by ensuring that the structure's foundations are deep enough. Frost damage above ground level can be minimized by careful design and construction, and by using special concrete or mortar mixes. These mixes encourage the formation of minute air bubbles in the concrete or mortar, thus reducing the damage caused by the expansion and contraction of freezing and thawing water and ice.

For all the advantages of bricks and concrete, amateurs often avoid using them because it looks like hard and strenuous work. This is not true. Some materials, of course, are undeniably heavy; a single concrete paving slab may weigh 20 kg, and a standard bag of cement weighs 50 kg. But most masonry and paving units are reasonably light, and even the heavy ones are safe and simple to handle with appropriate equipment, such as sturdy wheelbarrows and crowbars, and sensible methods, such as remembering to bend your legs rather than just your back for lifting, so that your legs take most of the strain. It is also advisable to wear sturdy clothing—heavy shoes to protect your feet, leather-palmed work gloves and overalls. Once these precautions have been taken, the main requirements for such jobs as laying and aligning the bricks for a garden wall are good planning, patience and precision—exactly the same requirements that you need to do a good job of carpentry or painting. Never rush the planning and preparation stages—once installed, bricks and concrete are exceptionally difficult to remove. To alter the dimensions of a concrete slab you may have to hire a powerful drill; any mistakes in building a brick wall will entail taking the wall down brick by brick and starting again.

The techniques involved in the projects in this book take only a few hours of practice to master. Most of them can be learnt while you are carrying out simple repairs to existing brickwork, concrete or asphalt *(pages 16–25)*. For extra assurance, practise the techniques on simple jobs before you decide to tackle major projects.

Some procedures—throwing a mortar line, for example—may look tricky at first sight. But in fact the "trick" boils down to nothing more difficult than twisting a trowel in such a way that mortar will slide off it to form an even ridge; the knack is easy for most people to acquire.

With new construction, in fact, you will find that the biggest part of the project may well be the preparation. Most of the projects involve excavations, although deep ones are seldom needed. For most concrete work you have to build simple wooden forms—temporary constructions that hold the concrete while it sets. In addition, many projects may require a building permit; while still at the planning stage, consult the local authority. To obtain approval, the plan for the proposed project may have to meet both design and structural standards.

Once the advance work has been accomplished, the job can be very simple. Many structures are built of regular-sized units that go together like the playthings that children use. Bricks, tiles and concrete blocks are available in standardized sizes—and in a wide variety of shapes, so that they can readily be fitted into the design of your choice. Some tiles even come already glued on to sheets, so that a whole sheet can be laid at one time, saving time and effort.

Beyond the simplicity that is introduced when modular units are employed, there is another great advantage: speed. The actual work proceeds at a fast pace because cement, the basic bonding agent that is used in nearly all cases, sets rock-hard in a matter of hours. Cement, which is manufactured from limestone and clay or shale, is a water-soluble bonding agent that holds sand together to form mortar or grout. Mortar and grout in turn bond bricks, blocks, tiles and stones into sturdy, solid structures.

Mortar applied as a thin veneer to exterior walls is known as rendering. When gravel or crushed stones are added to a mixture of cement, water and sand, the result is concrete. There is one masonry material that is made without cement: asphalt, which contains a crude-oil extract known as bitumen that acts as a bonding agent for crushed stone.

The speed with which these bonding agents set demands careful timing. That problem can be dealt with in the planning. To take the pressure off, and to put pleasure into doing a job carefully and expertly, most of the work described in this book can be planned in stages—and completed at a leisurely pace, one stage at a time.

Words Given a Craftsman's Twist

The bricklayer's and stonemason's speech may sound like English but to the uninitiated it could just as well be Martian, since common words have been given uncommon meanings, many only fancifully related to ordinary usage. In a few instances the word-stealing has gone the other way, and a bricklayer's term has acquired a new definition in general speech—the traditional headgear of the university scholar, for instance, is almost certainly named after the similar-looking square board used to hold mortar. Among the more colourful jargon:

BAT: A part-brick cut from a whole one. Half a brick is called a "half-bat" and quarter of a brick is a "quarter-bat".

BATTER: Slope of the face of a wall.

BLEEDING: The separation of water from freshly poured concrete. Allow this surface sheen of water to evaporate completely before finishing the concrete.

BOLSTER: A broad-bladed chisel used with a hammer to cut bricks, and to remove bricks or mortar from a wall.

BUTTER: To spread mortar on a brick before setting it in place. The term also describes the ideal consistency of mortar for bricklaying.

CLOSER: A brick or block which has been cut in order to complete the bonding pattern at the corner or end of a wall.

CURING: To keep concrete moist after it has been poured and finished. Concrete develops strength via a chemical reaction between the cement and the water in the mix—it does not harden by drying out. Curing concrete usually takes between three and four days.

DARBY: A large wooden float, about 1 metre long and 100 mm wide. Used to compact and level poured concrete.

FLOAT: A flat rectangular blade of steel or wood with a wooden handle attached to the back, which is used to smooth the surface of a concrete slab. A float with a very long handle is called a skip float.

FROG: An indentation on the bedding face or faces of a brick.

GREEN: The condition of concrete or mortar that has become stiff enough to hold its shape but has not yet developed any significant structural strength.

HAWK: A small, square, wooden or alloy tray, with a short handle fixed into the centre of the underside, which is used to hold mortar while pointing. The term may come from the board from which peddlers hawked their wares.

HEADER: A brick or block laid end-on to the face of a wall.

HOD: A long-handled, V-shaped trough used for carrying bricks or mortar.

POINT: To fill the outer part of a joint between the bricks or blocks with a mortar different to that used for the joint itself. To repoint is to remove crumbling mortar from old joints and repair them with new mortar.

RAKE: To scrape out mortar from the joints between bricks for decoration, or in order to repoint a wall.

RENDERING: A skin of mortar applied to exterior walls as weatherproofing or decoration.

SLURRY: A fluid mixture of cement and water used to fill fine cracks or as a bonding coat when laying bedding mortar on a concrete slab.

SOLDIER: A brick or block laid upright with its narrowest face outwards.

STRETCHER: A brick or block laid with its longest dimension parallel to the face of a wall.

Tool Kit for Bricks and Concrete

Building work requires general-purpose tools as well as some specialized ones that are used only with specific materials—concrete, brick, stone, block or tile. Most are widely available at hardware shops and builders' merchants, and some rarely used ones—such as a cartridge hammer or a quarry tile cutter—can be hired.

The most important general tools to buy are a metre-long spirit level, a steel square, a 10 or 20 metre measuring tape, a cold chisel for chipping mortar and concrete, and a club or lump hammer. Chisel and hammer can sometimes be replaced by a mortar rake—a specialized tool for removing crumbling mortar from a wall.

Special tools needed for concrete work include a small wood float for levelling; a steel float for smoother finishing; a darby or screed—a long narrow float, which you can make yourself by attaching a handle to a long, flat piece of wood—for smoothing large areas; and an edging tool, for rounding the sides of a slab.

To lay a true course of brick or block, a guide line is essential. You can support it either with pins—shown here—or with wooden blocks; pins are inserted into the joints between bricks, but blocks are held in place by the line's own tension, as shown on page 88. Other tools for laying and finishing a brick or block wall are a bricklayer's hammer and a broad-bladed chisel, called a bolster, for cutting; a small mortar board, called a hawk, to hold mortar close to the job; a bricklayer's trowel for spreading the mortar; a joint filler, sometimes called a finger or window trowel, for filling extra-long joints with mortar; a pointing trowel to fill joints and to form weathered, struck, flush and extruded joints; and a rounded jointing tool for concave joints.

A carbide-tipped masonry bit in an electric drill is useful for putting small holes in concrete blocks. For holes larger than 20 mm use a star drill, a kind of chisel meant to be struck with a hammer. When laying bricks on a horizontal surface—a patio, for example—use a V-notched square trowel to score the bed joint.

For tile work, you will need a square trowel with rectangular—or box—notches to score the bed joint. A pincer-like tile nipper can be used to shape the tiles.

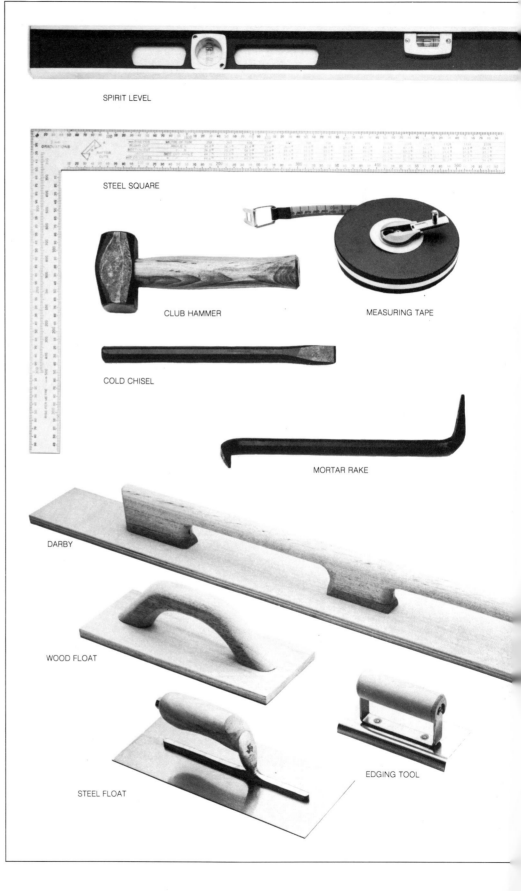

SPIRIT LEVEL

STEEL SQUARE

CLUB HAMMER

MEASURING TAPE

COLD CHISEL

MORTAR RAKE

DARBY

WOOD FLOAT

STEEL FLOAT

EDGING TOOL

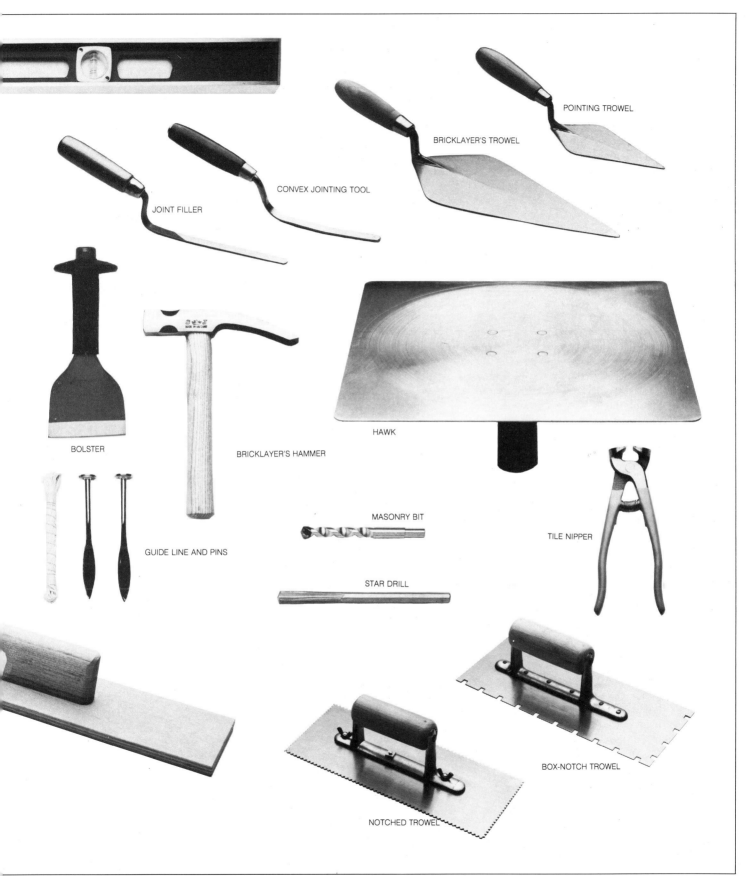

POINTING TROWEL

BRICKLAYER'S TROWEL

CONVEX JOINTING TOOL

JOINT FILLER

BOLSTER

BRICKLAYER'S HAMMER

HAWK

GUIDE LINE AND PINS

MASONRY BIT

STAR DRILL

TILE NIPPER

BOX-NOTCH TROWEL

NOTCHED TROWEL

Basic Techniques of Working with Mortar and Trowel

Mortar is the basic bonding material that holds bricks, stones and blocks together; a trowel is the essential tool for working with it. Once you master mixing and trowelling mortar, you can repair walls or paving, or launch more ambitious projects such as constructing a brick wall or laying a path with paving slabs.

For most purposes, you can produce workable mortar by following either of the two recipes on the right. Both are given in two strengths—a normal mix, for most mortaring jobs, and a strong mix, to be used for copings, sills, paving and walls made of heavy masonry units, such as dense concrete blocks or stone. In each case the proportions of the ingredients are given in the form of a ratio, by volume, which remains constant whatever the size of the mortar batch. The yield figures will help you to estimate the quantity of materials you will need to buy. When mixing mortar, remember that you only need roughly 0.01 cubic metres (about 2 kg cement, normal mix) to lay 25 to 30 bricks—as much as you are likely to have time to use before the mix hardens. With practice, however, you may be able to increase the size of the batch to lay about 60 bricks at a time.

The cement-lime mortar at its normal strength is frequently called a 1:1:6 mix, since it contains Portland cement, hydrated lime and sand in these proportions. It produces a good general-purpose mortar suitable for most weather conditions. The plasticized mortar differs from it in that the lime is replaced by a plasticizer, which is added to the sand before mixing. (The manufacturer's instructions will tell you how much to add.) The plasticizer makes the mortar more resistant to frost damage, so this mix should be used for work that is likely to be exposed to severe weather.

You can also get the ingredients pre-mixed in the form of dry mixes, sold under several brand names, to which only water need be added. The dry mixes are more expensive than ingredients purchased separately, but the cost may not matter when only small amounts are needed.

Sand for mortar can be any clean, dry, finely graded builder's—or soft—sand. Never use beach sand; it contains salts that will weaken and discolour the mortar and prevent it from drying properly.

The exact amount of water required for the mortar depends on the humidity and temperature as well as the moisture in the sand and cannot be computed in advance. Add water slowly in small amounts, stirring until it is all absorbed. But add as much water as possible without ruining the desired consistency. If the mortar is too wet, it will run out between joints; if it is too dry, it will not form a really tight bond.

While using the mortar, stir it often. If evaporation dries it out, add more water from time to time—a process called retempering—to restore its workability. Mortar that begins to set before use should be discarded. After the mortar has set—but before it hardens, usually within one or two hours—finish by compacting and shaping the joints between the bricks with a trowel or special finishing tool. Mortar only when the temperature is above 4°C.

When mixing mortar, wear leather-palmed work gloves to protect your hands from irritants in the cement; keep them on when buttering and laying bricks as well. But such finishing jobs as shaping mortar joints are best done barehanded.

For decorative effects, mortar can be coloured with the aid of pigments sold in powder or liquid form. Before beginning work with coloured mortar, make up a few sample batches using varying amounts of colour in each one. Let them set for several days before choosing the final colour; the mortar lightens as it dries. Follow the manufacturer's instructions when mixing, and keep a record of the ingredients in each sample so that you can duplicate the chosen colour in successive batches.

To give yourself the best chance of achieving uniform results with coloured mortar, bond the bricks first with ordinary mortar, then rake out the joints to a depth of 10 to 12 mm. When the wall is finished, use coloured mortar to finish the joints.

Mixing and Testing Recipes

	Cement-Lime Mortar		Plasticized Mortar	
	Ratio (by volume)	Yield of mortar per 50 kg cement	Ratio (by volume)	Yield of mortar per 50 kg cement
Normal mix	1 part Portland cement 1 part hydrated lime 6 parts sand	0.25 cubic metres	1 part Portland cement 5–6 parts sand with plasticizer	0.24 cubic metres
Strong mix	1 part Portland cement ½ part hydrated lime 4–4½ parts sand	0.19 cubic metres	1 part Portland cement 3–4 parts sand with plasticizer	0.16 cubic metres

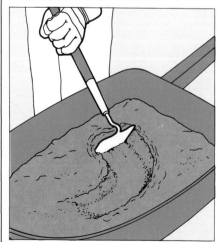

Making a batch of mortar. Measure sand into a wheelbarrow and add lime or plasticizer. With a hoe or shovel, make a crater in the centre and add the cement, mixing until the colour is uniform. Make another crater and add water, mixing well by drawing the dry material towards the wet until all lumps are eliminated.

You can expect to use about half a litre of water for every kilogram of cement. Add water slowly until the mortar is like soft butter. To test the consistency, make a curved furrow on the surface with a hoe. If the furrow's sides stay in place and the mortar shakes freely off the hoe, the mix is ready. If the furrow collapses, the mix is too wet—add small amounts of the dry materials. If the mortar does not shake freely off the hoe, it is too dry—add small amounts of water, testing the consistency each time.

Making a Bed of Mortar

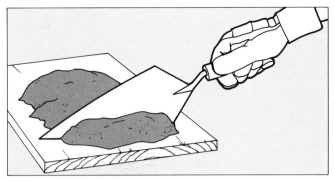

1 Cutting off a slice of mortar. Take enough mixed mortar from the mixing container to form a mound in the centre of a mortar board or a 300 mm square piece of plywood. To separate a slice of mortar from the mound, grasp the trowel handle between your thumb and forefinger, with your thumb resting along the top and your fingers clasping the handle. With your hand, wrist and forearm relaxed, drop the edge of the trowel into the mortar.

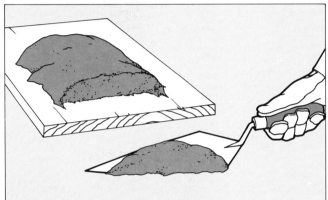

2 Loading the trowel. With a twist of your wrist, sweep the trowel blade under the slice and scoop the mortar on to one side of the blade so that a wedge of mortar lies on this part of the blade. Shake the trowel sharply downwards to firm the loaded mortar into a neat sausage-like lump—a messy heap is much more difficult to handle.

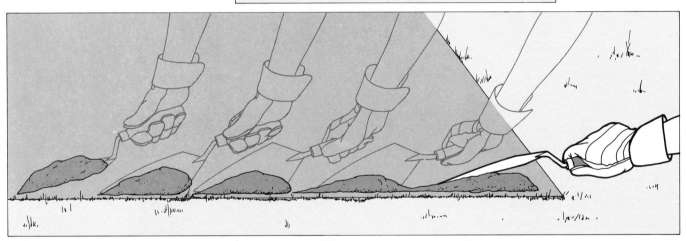

3 Throwing the mortar. Set the point of the trowel, face up, where you want to begin the mortar line *(above)*. Bring the trowel towards you and rotate the blade 180 degrees: the mortar will roll off and form a straight line, about one brick wide and several bricks long. The mortar line should be about 20 mm thick. If the line is not straight, return the mortar to the board and repeat the throwing action. With practice, you should be able to form a line four bricks long.

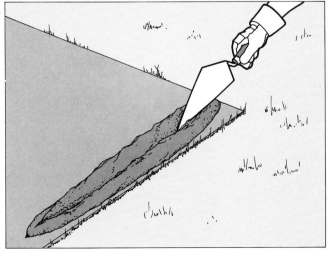

4 Furrowing the mortar. Immediately after throwing the mortar line, run the point of the trowel down the centre of the line to make a shallow furrow. This small depression helps form a steady bond by spreading the mortar outwards slightly so that when the brick is pressed down on it the mortar will be evenly distributed.

Laying the Bricks

Beginning a row. Start at a corner, placing the first brick, dampened with a hose-pipe set at a fine spray, frog-upwards on the mortar bed *(page 13)* just inside the end of the mortar line. Push the brick about 10 mm into the mortar. With a spirit level, check that the brick is aligned horizontally across its length and width, as well as vertically. If not, tap it with the trowel handle and test again; replace the brick if necessary. Check with the level frequently while working.

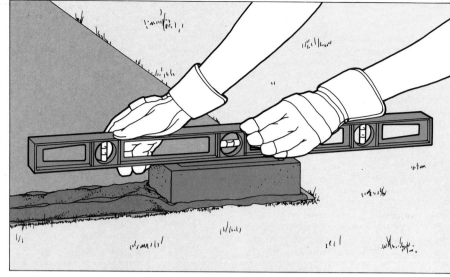

Buttering intermediate bricks. Between the ends of a row, butter adjoining brick surfaces. For end-to-end bricks in a "stretcher course", scoop up enough mortar to cover the end; for side-to-side bricks in a "header course", scoop up enough to cover the side. Spread the mortar 15 mm thick and remove any excess that slides over the edges.

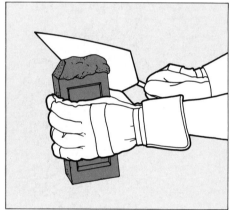

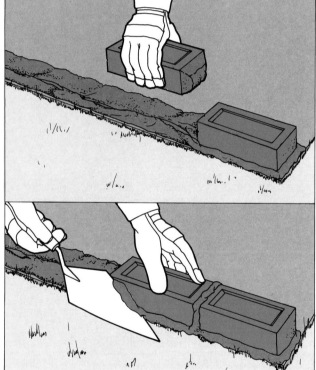

Laying intermediate bricks. Place the buttered brick in the mortar bed with the buttered end or side next to the end brick laid first *(right, above)*. In one motion, push the brick down 10 mm into the bed and towards the first brick to form a 10 mm joint between them. With the edge of your trowel, trim off mortar that has oozed out of the joints *(right)* and return it to the mortar board.

Laying the closure brick. Work from the ends of the course towards the middle, until there is room for only one more brick. Spread a 15 mm layer of mortar on the ends of the last two bricks and, if necessary, add more mortar to the bed. Butter both ends of the closure brick and insert it into the opening *(right)*. Push the brick into the bed and trim off excess mortar at the joints. In an hour or two, finish the joints. Of the joints on the opposite page, only those that shed water well are recommended for outdoor use. Use raked and struck joints only indoors or in dry climates.

Finishing the Joints

Concave. This is the most popular of all joints because it sheds rainwater and, since mortar is forced tightly between the bricks, makes an excellent bond. To shape it, press the mortar firmly with anything that fits; a convex jointing tool, a dowel, a metal rod or even a teaspoon.

V joint. This type of joint stands out as a sharp line that directs water off. Form it with a V-shaped jointer, a suitable bit of wood or the tip of a pointing trowel.

Raked or recessed. Forming a square recess, this joint does not shed water, but casts a heavy shadow to accentuate brick courses. To form the joint, remove 5 to 7 mm of mortar with a raking tool or a piece of wood, then smooth the surface with a stick. New joints can be bonded with plain mortar, raked out to a depth of 10 to 12 mm, then finished with white or coloured mortar *(page 12)*.

Weathered. This type sheds rainwater more efficiently than any other joint shown here because it is recessed from the bottom to the top. It is formed by working from below the joint. Hold the blade of the trowel at an angle and compress the mortar from the front edge of the bottom brick upwards to a point 5 mm inside the top brick.

Struck. This joint is not water-resistant because its recess slants from top to bottom. To shape it, hold the blade of the trowel at an angle and compress the mortar approximately 5 mm away from the forward edge of the lower brick.

Flush. This joint is not water-resistant because the mortar is not compacted. It is the joint that is left if you simply trowel off excess mortar after bricks are laid. For the neatest results, form the joint when the mortar has set slightly, taking care not to stain the bricks with mortar.

Extruded. Also called a weeping joint, this type is not water-resistant but gives masonry a rustic appearance. It is created by laying new bricks with an excess of mortar; when the bricks are put into place the mortar is squeezed out and hangs down. To reproduce this effect when replacing old mortar, build up joints with excess mortar.

The Professional's Tricks for Simple Repairs

The monuments of the ancients prove that masonry can endure for millennia. But if its original attractiveness is to survive, cracks and crumbled sections must be repaired promptly—especially in cold climates. Even a hairline crack will allow moisture to penetrate a wall or slab and, by freezing and thawing, spread destruction.

Repairing such damage is a simple process with mortar or grout. The techniques shown here for repairing bricks, blocks, concrete and rendering apply to paths and patios as well as walls—only the direction of the work changes. But the method employed depends on the defect. Three types are most common: crumbling mortar in joints; a broken section of a wall; and deteriorating concrete steps and paths.

If you notice crumbling mortar joints in old walls, repair them by repointing: chisel out the old mortar and replace it with new.

If the bricks are cracked or have broken out of the wall, replace both bricks and mortar. On both of these jobs you can make the repairs almost invisible by finishing new joints to match existing ones.

Mortar shrinks as it dries out and this can cause cracks along the joints in new structures. New clay bricks used straight from the supplier will expand slightly as they take up moisture. This should be sufficient to close up fine cracks. However, new blocks or bricks made of concrete (or a sand-lime mixture) will shrink for some time. Wait until such a crack has stabilized, then make it good by repointing *(below)* or by filling it with slurry. To make slurry, mix cement with water until fluid enough to be pressed into the crack.

A wide crack, or one that opens up after being filled in, could indicate serious structural weakness. Do not try to repair such a crack in a loadbearing or high wall but seek professional advice at once. A broad crack in a low, non-loadbearing wall can be patched with grout *(page 19)*.

Broken concrete paths or cracked steps are too dangerous to leave unrepaired. The kind of material used to mend them varies according to the dimensions and the type of defect *(pages 20–23)*. Small cracks, for example, can be filled with grout; large ones require mortar. When large pieces, still intact, break off steps, you can glue them on again with resin adhesive. But when sections of steps crumble away, you will have to build them up again with mortar.

In any job, remember that mortar and grout must be kept damp for three to four days to form a strong bond. Keep the repair covered, if possible, and sprinkle it with water as necessary—at least four or five times a day in hot, dry weather.

Replacing Damaged Mortar

1 **Cleaning out the joint.** With a cold chisel and a hammer, remove crumbling mortar from a joint to a depth of about 15 mm. To ensure an effective bond, chop out enough additional mortar to expose bare brick on one side of every joint. Brush out the joints thoroughly to remove dust and loose particles. Caution: goggles are absolutely necessary to protect your eyes.

2 **Laying the mortar.** Dampen the joints with a small, wet brush or a hose-pipe set at a fine spray. Spread a 10 mm thick layer of mortar *(page 12)* on a hawk—a small mortar board with a handle to hold it up to the work. With the bottom edge of a pointing trowel, which is smaller than an ordinary bricklayer's trowel, slice off a thin piece of mortar and press it into the joint. Because you push mortar away from you when pointing, always use the bottom of the trowel. For extra-long horizontal joints, you may want to use a joint filler.

If a large area needs to be repaired, point only two square metres at a time. Work from top to bottom and left to right, and take care not to stain the bricks with the new mortar.

Splitting Bricks

Crosswise cuts. Most brick jobs will probably require you to cut some bricks into smaller sections. With a pencil and ruler, mark a cutting line all round the brick. Mark on the diagonal (*inset*) if this shape is required, but remember that diagonals are more difficult to cut cleanly. Wear goggles to protect your eyes from chips. Cushion the brick on a bed of sand, and position it lengthwise on its side so that the part you intend to use faces you. Place the blade of a bolster—a broad-bladed chisel—on the cutting line and tap the handle with a hammer. Score a progressively deeper groove round the brick. Listen to the sound as you work. When the brick begins to split, the sound will lose its resonance and the cut can be finished with a sharp tap. Chop off any irregularities with a trowel.

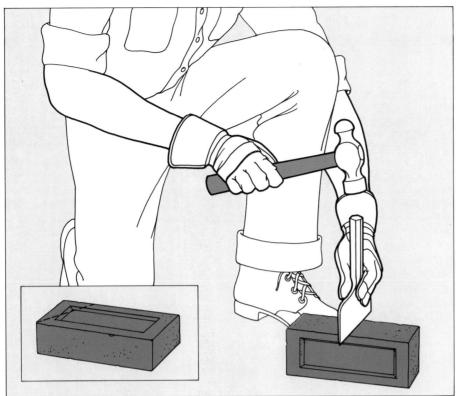

Lengthwise cuts. Find the centre point of one of the long side edges of the brick. Measure and mark a continuous cutting line all round the brick. Wearing goggles, score the surface along the cutting line by tapping the line with the sharp edge of the square end of a bricklayer's hammer—or, for extra-hard bricks, with a bolster—as shown above. Grip the brick firmly in one hand, and strike the brick sharply with the flat side of the square end of the hammer, just beyond the centre point of the scored line. (You may have to practise this technique several times before you can halve the brick neatly with a single blow.) Use the curved, chisel-like blade end of the hammer to clean off rough spots on the cut edges, removing small bits at a time.

Cutting bricks lengthwise is trickier than cutting across. If you have a power tool, you can make the work easier by using an abrasive disc attachment in place of a hammer and bolster to cut the groove round the brick. When you have scored each surface, finish off the cut by tapping sharply with a hammer and bolster.

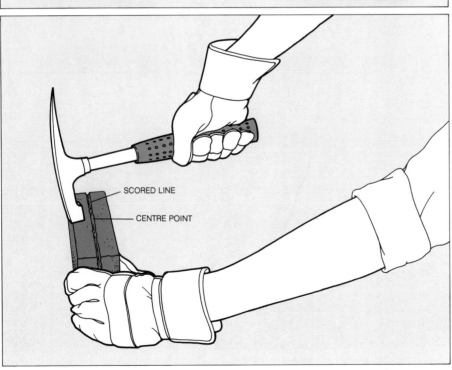

SCORED LINE

CENTRE POINT

Replacing a Broken Brick

1 **Removing a single damaged brick.** Rip out mortar with a mortar rake—a valuable tool if you can find one—or a cold chisel and hammer. Because the mortar rake enables you to use both hands, it speeds up the job. Chisel out the damaged brick and brush the space clean.

2 **Replacing the brick.** Select or cut a brick to fit the slot. Dampen the slot and apply a thick coating of mortar. Hold the brick on a hawk or mortar board about 15 mm above the course the brick will rest on. Ram the brick into the slot. Trowel in extra mortar if needed to fill the joints.

Filling In a Damaged Wall

Cutting out and replacing bricks. Remove all mortar surrounding damaged bricks and chop out all broken or cracked bricks with a bolster and a hammer. When removing adjoining bricks, work from the top of the damaged area downwards. Brush away bits of mortar, brick and dust. Working from the bottom course upwards, dampen all surfaces of both old and replace- ment bricks, then lay down mortar beds for the replacement bricks, trowelling and furrowing the bed just as you would for placing new bricks. Butter the bricks and lay them in place on the mortar beds. When the mortar is firm, finish the joints so that they match the rest of the wall *(page 15)*. Keep the new mortar wet for three to four days, until it has cured.

Patching a Large
Vertical Crack with Grout

1 Pouring the grout. A long, broad, vertical crack in
a low, non-loadbearing wall can be filled more
quickly by pouring grout into it than by laying
in mortar with a trowel. First, clean the crack.
Mix mortar in a bucket, adding just enough
water for the mortar to flow easily through a
wide funnel. Do not add more water than necessary—the more water you add, the more the
grout will shrink as it hardens. Dampen the
bricks round the crack with a wet brush. Then
cover the lowest section of the crack with a piece
of wide heavy-duty adhesive tape, 300 to 500 mm
long. Pour grout from the bucket into the taped
section, using a wide funnel *(right)*. If necessary,
push the grout through the funnel with a rod.
Work upwards section by section to fill more of
the crack in the same way, but do not try to
repair more than about a metre at a time.

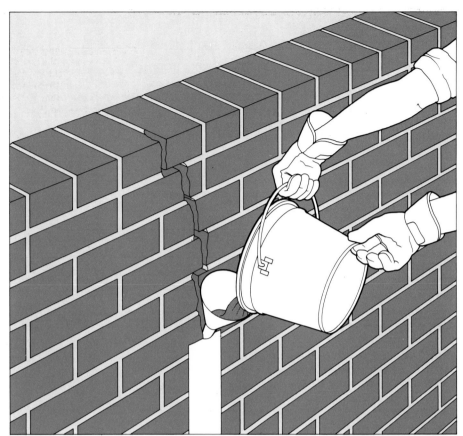

2 Shoring up the grout. A crack filled with tape-held
grout needs reinforcement to hold the grout in
place while it is wet. Brace a board over the tape
until the grout sets, usually two to three hours.
Provide the reinforcement immediately after
filling each section if the tape does not adhere
well—on rough bricks for example. Otherwise
the board backing will not be required until you
have filled about a metre of the crack.

Caution: this technique should not be used in
repairing a loadbearing or high wall. Even a
narrow crack in such a wall may be a sign of
structural weakness, and professional advice
should therefore be sought.

How to Restore Concrete

Paradoxically, concrete cannot be repaired with concrete—the coarse aggregate in the new material would prevent a strong bond between the patch and the damaged area. Instead, the materials to use are cement slurry (a mixture of cement and water), cement mortar containing a bonding agent, epoxy or polyester resin mortar, or a proprietary patching compound.

Before using any of these materials, remove all damaged concrete, dirt, dust and standing water from the repair area. With cement-based mortars, keep the area to be treated moist for several hours, preferably overnight. If you use a resin mortar or a proprietary patching mix, prepare the surface according to the manufacturer's instructions. Before repairing the edge of a concrete slab, set up form boards to support the fresh concrete while it cures.

For cracks up to 3 mm wide, use slurry or a proprietary patching compound. Mixes sold in a cartridge can be applied directly with a caulking gun. Slurry, or a tinned mix, must be forced into the crack with a trowel or a putty knife and smoothed flush with the surrounding concrete.

Mend larger cracks or chipped concrete in the same way, with a proprietary patching compound or a mix of 1 part Portland cement or high-alumina cement, 3 parts sand, and water to which you have added a bonding agent such as polyvinyl acetate (PVA) or synthetic rubber latex (SBR) according to the maker's instructions. (High-alumina cement, also known as *ciment fondu*, differs chemically from Portland cement, and gains strength rapidly.) If the concrete has spalled—flaked off in thin scales—either break up the surface to a depth of 10 to 15 mm before patching, or use a resin mortar which, although expensive, produces a very durable repair.

Let a repair made with cement slurry or mortar set for two to three hours until firm to the touch; keep it moist for about three days while it cures. Mixes made from Portland cement should be covered with a plastic sheet secured round the edges with bricks or stones; mixes made from high-alumina cement should be protected with sacking and kept wet by frequent sprinkling. Cure other repair compounds according to the maker's instructions.

Treating Wide Cracks

1 Removing the damaged concrete. Chip away all cracked or crumbling concrete to a depth of about 20 mm below the surface, using a cold chisel and a hammer. Wear goggles during this and the next step to protect your eyes.

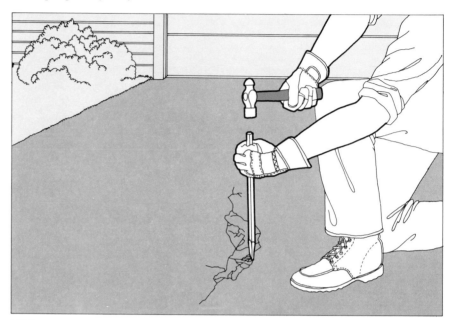

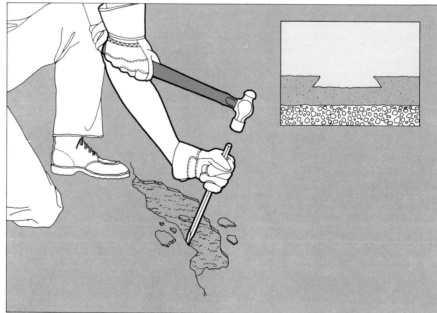

2 Undercutting the edges. To provide a better bond and keep the patch from heaving upwards after the job is done, undercut the edges of the crack with the hammer and chisel until the hole you have made is wider at the bottom than at the top *(inset)*. Remove all rubble and dirt. Soak the crack for several hours; if possible, run a trickle from a hose-pipe through it overnight.

3 **Priming the surface.** Thoroughly mix 1 part cement, 3 parts sand, and water containing a bonding agent such as PVA or SBR into a paste stiff enough to work with a trowel, and set it aside. Using a paintbrush, coat the area to be repaired with bonding agent thinned with water according to the maker's instructions. Proceed immediately to Step 4; the repair must be completed before the bonding agent dries.

4 **Filling the crack with mortar.** Pack the mortar into the crack with a bricklayer's trowel, compacting the mixture to remove air pockets. Level the mortar with a steel float until it begins to stiffen, then spread it evenly backwards and forwards across the crack, always with the leading edge of the float slightly raised *(below)*. To cure the patch, follow the procedure described in the text on the opposite page.

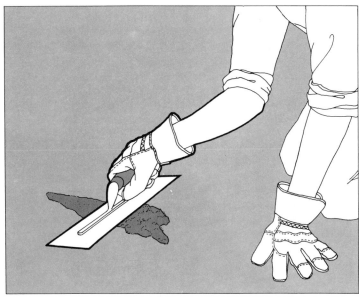

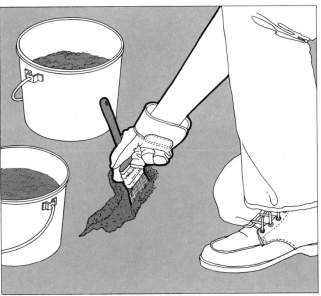

Refinishing Spalled Surfaces

Using a resin mix. Wearing goggles to protect your eyes from flying fragments, break up large areas of scaling concrete with a sledge-hammer (let the hammer drop of its own weight rather than swinging it hard against the surface); for small areas, use a hammer and a cold chisel. Sweep up dust and debris, using a stiff wire brush to dislodge any small fragments.

Follow the manufacturer's instructions on preparing the surface and mixing the resin mortar. Apply the mixture with a steel float, bringing the new layer level with the surrounding concrete and feathering it thinly at the edges. Protect the patch from any pressure for three to four days until it has cured.

Putting Back a Broken Step

1 Gluing the broken piece. Brush particles of dirt and cement from the broken piece and the damaged corner of the step. Mix a small batch of resin-based masonry adhesive, following the directions on the label and, with a trowel, coat the part of the piece that will face the step. Position the piece and hold it firmly until the glue has hardened. The instructions on the packet will tell you how long this should take. If necessary, prop a board against the piece to hold it in place.

2 Completing the job. After the glue has set, use a scraper or putty knife to remove any excess that has oozed out between the piece and the step. You will probably find a small, irregular crack round the repair; patch it as you would any narrow crack, but use resin mortar rather than slurry. Avoid stepping on the repaired corner or bumping against it for at least 24 hours to allow the mortar to harden completely.

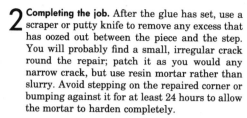

Rebuilding the Corner of a Step

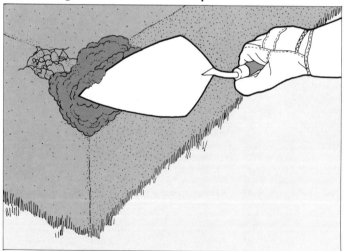

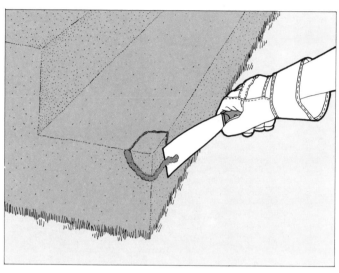

1 Shaping a replacement piece. If the corner of the step has crumbled away or been lost, clean and moisten the damaged edge. Mix 1 part cement with 3 parts sand and add just enough water and bonding agent to make a paste that holds its shape. Prime the damaged surface with bonding agent and, with a trowel, apply the mortar in the approximate shape of the original corner. Let the mortar harden until it retains a firmly impressed thumbprint (this may take up to six hours, depending on weather conditions).

2 Finishing the corner. Finish and smooth the corner flush to the adjoining parts of the step with a steel float. Let the mortar cure for three days under plastic sheeting or damp sacking. Moisten it twice a day, and avoid stepping on the corner or bumping it for another week or two. (Mortar made with high-alumina cement will support kicks and bumps after a few days.)

Repairing the Chipped Edge of a Step

1 **Clearing the damage.** With a hammer and a cold chisel held horizontally, chip off the damaged concrete all the way across the edge of the step. Be sure to wear goggles to protect your eyes from flying fragments of concrete.

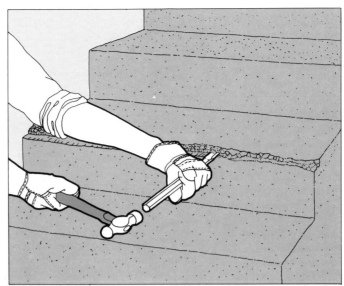

2 **Undercutting a groove.** Still wearing the goggles, but holding the chisel at an angle, chip away enough of the step to make a V-shaped groove *(inset)*. Clean off all debris and keep the edge damp for several hours, preferably overnight.

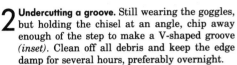

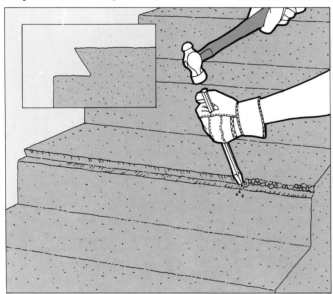

3 **Rebuilding the edge.** Thoroughly mix 1 part cement with 3 parts sand, then add just enough water and bonding agent to make a paste that holds its shape; set this mortar aside. Make a form board as wide and high as the riser and set it against the step, holding it in place with heavy objects such as bricks or concrete blocks. Coat the edge of the step with bonding agent *(page 21, Step 3)*, then immediately fill the V-shaped groove with mortar, shaping and smoothing it flush to the adjoining surfaces with a steel float.

4 **Completing the job.** Let the mortar set for about an hour, finish the step to a rounded edge with an edging tool, then carefully remove the board. Keep the area damp for at least a week to help the mortar cure, and do not step on the new edge for another five to seven days.

Renovating Damaged Rendering

Rendering is simply a thin skin of mortar applied to exterior walls as weatherproofing or decoration. It may be smooth or textured, or have pebbles embedded in it. Whatever the finish, it is essential to keep rendering in good repair, because even tiny cracks may enable moisture to penetrate, causing large sections to fall away. A damaged area larger than half a square metre, or a wall where much of the rendering is crumbling, is best repaired by a professional, but small patches can often be repaired using much the same methods as for other forms of wall repair.

Fill very fine cracks with exterior-grade filler—choose one that matches the colour of the rendering as closely as possible. Larger areas of damage can be patched following the recipe for 1:1:6 mortar on page 12, with the addition of a bonding agent such as PVA or SBR *(page 20)*. Alternatively, use a dry-mix rendering mortar, available from builders' merchants. As a rule, mortar for rendering should be slightly stiffer than bricklaying mortar.

It is difficult to patch rendering inconspicuously. If you are working on an unpainted surface and your patch does not blend in with the original, disguise it by painting the whole surface with masonry paint or exterior-grade emulsion 24 hours after patching. When patching a wall that has already been painted, paint the patch to match or repaint the entire wall.

If the original rendering is not painted but is coloured with pigments added to the mortar *(page 12)*, you will have to treat your repair likewise. Matching the original colour by this method is difficult. Mix a small batch of mortar and let it dry before judging the colour match, then make closer matches by trial and error.

While the rendering is still damp, you can give a patch a textured finish with a wooden float *(Step 3)*. To create a finer texture, fasten a piece of carpet or plastic foam to the base of the float; for a coarser finish, score the surface with a broom. If the surrounding area is pebble-dashed, press matching pebbles on to the patch when it is wet and push them in lightly with a float.

1 **Preparing the surface.** Wearing goggles to protect your eyes from flying fragments, use a bolster and hammer or a stripping knife to scrape away damaged rendering until you reach a firm layer, if necessary working right down to the base. To avoid damaging underlying brickwork, hold the bolster at a slight angle. If the base is composed of smooth concrete or engineering bricks, roughen the surface with the bolster to provide a good key. Undercut the edges of the area to be repaired, remove loose material with a wire brush and keep the damaged area damp overnight.

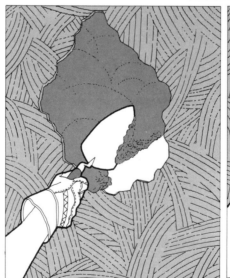

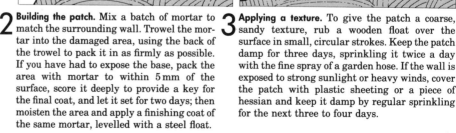

2 **Building the patch.** Mix a batch of mortar to match the surrounding wall. Trowel the mortar into the damaged area, using the back of the trowel to pack it in as firmly as possible. If you have had to expose the base, pack the area with mortar to within 5 mm of the surface, score it deeply to provide a key for the final coat, and let it set for two days; then moisten the area and apply a finishing coat of the same mortar, levelled with a steel float.

3 **Applying a texture.** To give the patch a coarse, sandy texture, rub a wooden float over the surface in small, circular strokes. Keep the patch damp for three days, sprinkling it twice a day with the fine spray of a garden hose. If the wall is exposed to strong sunlight or heavy winds, cover the patch with plastic sheeting or a piece of hessian and keep it damp by regular sprinkling for the next three to four days.

First Aid for Holes in Asphalt

The asphalt used on roads, drives and paths is similar to concrete—a mixture of crushed stone or gravel aggregate mixed with a binder. In this case, however, the binder is not cement but a crude-oil extract called bitumen. Although asphalt is long-lasting, it will develop cracks and holes as a result of the action of frost, ice-melting salts or even oil dripping from cars. Asphalt is also vulnerable to the ultra-violet rays in sunlight, which gradually destroy the bitumen, making the surface friable.

To combat such deterioration, asphalt should be coated every four to five years, or when the surface breaks up, with a specially formulated waterproof sealer that is resistant to chemicals. If the surface is allowed to become too crumbly, the asphalt will have to be completely renewed. To apply the sealer, simply pour it straight from the can on to the asphalt and spread it evenly with a stiff broom.

This coating process will rebind loose surface aggregate, and also fill any cracks up to 5 mm wide. Larger cracks up to 15 mm wide should be filled with a specially formulated, ready-to-use crack filler before the sealer is applied. If the cracks are as much as 25 mm across, you may still be able to use crack filler, but thickened with sand to a putty-like consistency. Follow the instructions on the can carefully. Keep traffic off the surface for several hours after the sealer has been applied.

While sealer will fill most cracks, holes in an asphalt surface must be mended with a proprietary "cold-mix" asphalt, as illustrated on the right. Sold under a variety of brand names, these ready-mixed materials can be used direct from the container.

Whatever substance you are working with, it is best not to mend or reseal asphalt when the temperature is below 5°C. If cool weather has hardened the cold mix into an unworkable lump, soften it by standing the container by a water heater for a couple of hours before opening it.

How to Use Prepared Cold Mixes

1 Preparing the hole for repair. With a shovel or a hammer and chisel, dig out the hole to a depth of 30 mm or down to undamaged material, whichever is the deeper. Remove any loose material. Cut back the edges of the hole to sound asphalt, making sure that the sides of the hole are as straight as possible. Compact the bottom of the hole with a tamper made by fastening a pair of large door handles to opposite sides of a sturdy piece of wood.

2 Adding the asphalt. Fill the hole half way with cold-mix asphalt. Slice through the asphalt with a shovel to open air pockets, then compact the asphalt with the tamper. Add a second layer of asphalt, filling the hole until it is slightly proud of the surrounding surface. Compact the patch with the tamper or the back of a spade. Keep traffic off the new surface for a couple of days.

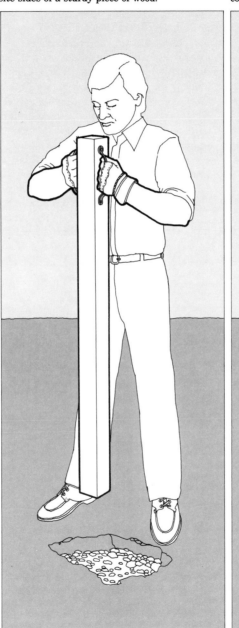

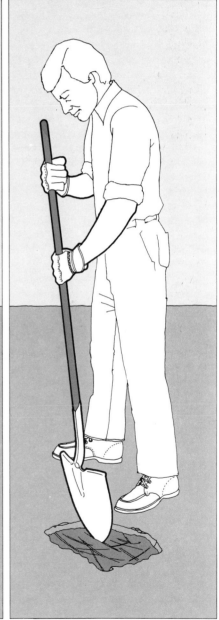

Home-Made Concrete in Convenient Batches

Concrete is man-made stone. Properly prepared, it will last nearly as long as natural stone and stand up to almost any punishment. Its strength comes from the materials: gravel or crushed stone (coarse aggregate), sand (fine aggregate), and Portland cement. The coarse aggregate supplies bulk; the sand fills voids between the coarse pieces; and the cement, moistened with water, binds the aggregate into a durable solid.

Concrete hardens, or cures, slowly and it is important to keep it moist for the first few days after it has been poured. The hardening starts one to two hours after mixing, depending on the temperature, and although it is no longer workable at this stage, it is still weak. It takes about three days to develop any real strength; one week to acquire half its full strength; and a month to reach its final strength.

Three basic grades of concrete—general purpose, foundation and paving—will meet most needs. The general-purpose mix suits most jobs, including paths, patios and concrete steps. It should not, however, be used for exposed paving in very cold climates or where the concrete may come into contact with de-icing salts of the type used on roads in cold weather, which can cause flaking or spalling. The general-purpose mix is not, therefore, suitable for drives.

The foundation mix, which contains a lower proportion of cement in relation to aggregate, can be used wherever concrete is laid underground. It is suitable for footings for walls and anchors for posts.

The paving mix contains the highest proportion of cement and should be used for small areas of *in situ* paving which may be exposed to severe weather conditions or to de-icing salts. For larger jobs under these conditions, use air-entrained concrete which contains additives that produce and trap—or entrain—microscopic air bubbles. When the concrete is wet, the bubbles act like tiny ball bearings to facilitate pouring and spreading. Once it hardens, the spaces created by the bubbles allow it to expand and contract with a minimum of cracking. Air-entrained concrete is normally available only to professionals. If you need to use it, order it from a ready-mix supplier *(page 41)*.

Be sure cement is dry before you buy it. If a bag is hard round the edges, its contents have probably absorbed moisture but are acceptable—rolling the bag on the ground will generally break up the lumps. If the edges do not break, however, or if you find any lumps inside that do not break between your fingers, choose another bag.

Choose sharp, concreting sand and coarse aggregate 20 mm in diameter. It is best to purchase these aggregates separately, but you can save time by buying blended all-in aggregate, commonly known as ballast. Be careful to avoid unwashed, "as-dug" ballast since this may contain substances that will weaken the concrete. For small jobs it is easier, but more expensive, to purchase a dry mix to which only water need be added.

The quantity of water required for a concrete recipe is critical; even a small amount extra can weaken the concrete. Sand almost always contains some water and this will affect how much you need to add. Normally, water content should not be more than half the cement content by weight. Start by adding only one-third as much water as cement and then adjust the quantity by testing as you mix *(page 29)*. You will probably need to add less water in later batches since there is usually more moisture at the bottom of a heap of sand.

How you mix the materials depends on how much concrete you need. A small amount of concrete can be mixed by hand in a wheelbarrow, or on a sheet of plywood or other hard, flat surface. But to mix enough concrete to build steps or a footing for a wall, hire a petrol or electric-powered mixer. Working with a power mixer, you should be able to pour and finish about 1 square metre of a 150 mm thick slab before the concrete hardens too much to be finished. For larger quantities, have ready-mixed concrete delivered *(page 41)*.

The table below provides recipes for mixing the three grades of concrete on site and gives the proportions of the ingredients by volume. The table also gives the weight of each ingredient needed to produce 1 cubic metre of concrete and the approximate yield per 50 kg of cement.

Three Basic Recipes

	Ratio (by volume)	Weight required to make 1 cubic metre of concrete	Yield of concrete per 50 kg cement
General purpose mix	1 part Portland cement	320 kg	0.16 cubic metres
	AND		
	EITHER 2 parts sand	680 kg	
	3 parts coarse aggregate	1175 kg	
	OR 4 parts combined aggregate	1855 kg	
Foundation mix	1 part Portland cement	280 kg	0.18 cubic metres
	AND		
	EITHER 2½ parts sand	720 kg	
	3½ parts coarse aggregate	1165 kg	
	OR 5 parts combined aggregate	1885 kg	
Paving mix	1 part Portland cement	400 kg	0.12 cubic metres
	AND		
	EITHER 1½ parts sand	600 kg	
	2½ parts coarse aggregate	1200 kg	
	OR 3½ parts combined aggregate	1800 kg	

Getting the Materials Ready to Use

Keeping the ingredients separate. Deposit cement, sand and coarse aggregate close to the work site. To prevent the cement from absorbing moisture, stack the bags against one another on a raised platform away from walls. On plastic sheeting or a tarpaulin, pile sand and coarse aggregate into two mounds, separated by a board divider if necessary. If the materials must be kept for more than a few hours, store them under cover or place all the cement bags inside plastic bags and cover them with a tarpaulin. Do not stockpile more than you can use in a week.

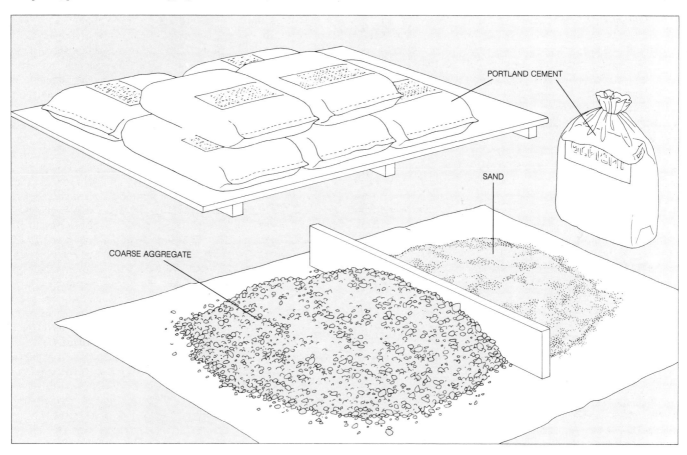

PORTLAND CEMENT

SAND

COARSE AGGREGATE

An Extra Ingredient: Built-In Colour

Concrete does not have to be plain grey. You can coat the top with a layer of coloured mortar while it is still wet *(pages 50–51)*, and you can, of course, paint or stain it after it cures. But the best way is to build colour in by adding pigments when you mix the concrete.

Using pigmented cement distributes particles of colour evenly throughout the mixture. This method, though, requires the use of a power mixer. If you try to mix pigmented cement with the aggregate and water by hand, the result is likely to be a mottled shade.

Pre-coloured cement may be hard to find (and expensive) but you can create your own by adding pigments made for colouring concrete to either grey or—for clearer tones—white Portland cement. These pigments cost more than natural metallic oxides, but are less likely to bleach or fade. They come in a range of colours you can use as they are, or combine to produce custom shades.

To ensure that colouring is uniform from batch to batch, measure pigments—and all other concrete ingredients—by weight, not volume. Use bathroom scales, wrapped in clear plastic to keep them clean and readable, for weighing; 10 to 15 litre buckets are a convenient size to hold the ingredients.

Concrete lightens as it dries, so finding the right amount of pigment to use will take experimentation. About 100 g of pigment and 10 kg of white—not grey—Portland cement will produce a pastel; 100 to 300 g to 10 kg of cement will produce a medium shade; 400 to 900 g to 10 kg of cement will produce a dark colour. To avoid weakening the concrete, never add more than 10 per cent pigment.

Mixing Concrete in a Wheelbarrow

1 Measuring the materials. Make no more than one wheelbarrow-sized batch of concrete—roughly 0.04 cubic metres—at a time. Measure out each of the ingredients (recipes, page 26) into a bucket. Use separate buckets for the cement and the aggregates.

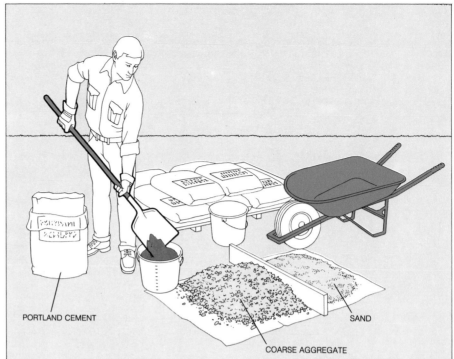

PORTLAND CEMENT

COARSE AGGREGATE

SAND

2 Combining the dry materials. Pour the sand into the wheelbarrow and, using a hoe, shape it into a ring. Pour the cement into the centre of the sand ring, then mix the ingredients. When the mixture is uniform in colour—without streaks of brown or grey—shape another ring. Pour coarse aggregate into the centre. Mix until the coarse aggregate is evenly distributed.

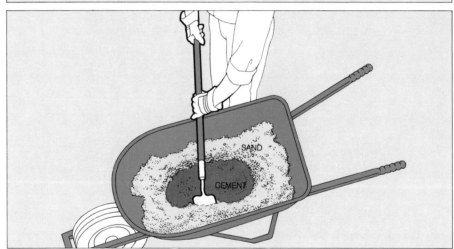

SAND

CEMENT

3 Adding the water. Push the sand-cement-coarse aggregate mixture to the sides of the wheelbarrow to form a bowl-like depression. Slowly pour about half the water into the depression (right). Pull the dry materials from the edges of the ring into the water, working all round the pile until the water is absorbed by the mixture. When no water remains standing on the surface, turn the concrete three or four times. Add more water a little at a time until the mixture completely coats all the coarse aggregate and the colour and consistency of the mix is uniform. Keep any unused water in the measuring bucket until after you test the consistency of the concrete and make necessary corrections. At the end of the day, clean up as explained on page 37.

CEMENT-SAND-COARSE AGGREGATE MIXTURE

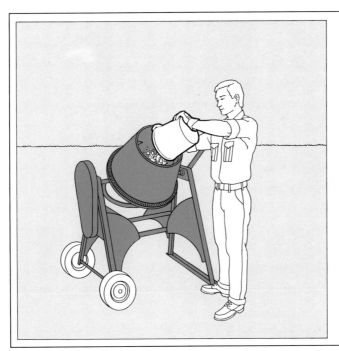

A Power Mixer to Make the Job Go Faster

Combining the ingredients. Before turning on the mixer, make sure that it is stable. Set the drum to the mixing position. Pour in half the expected amount of water *(page 26)* and half the coarse aggregate. Switch the mixer on, let it turn for a few moments, and add most of the sand and cement. Add the remaining quantities of each ingredient alternately in small amounts. Mix for at least two minutes. When it is ready, the mixture should be uniform in consistency and colour and should completely coat the coarse aggregate. Test a few shovelfuls in a wheelbarrow *(below)*, and return the test batch to the mixer before making corrections. When the concrete is ready, dump it into your wheelbarrow and hose out the drum. When you finish using the mixer, clean it thoroughly as described on page 37.

Testing the Consistency

Judging and correcting the mix. Smooth the concrete in your wheelbarrow by sliding the bottom of a shovel or trowel across the concrete's surface *(left)*. Then jab the edge of the shovel or trowel into the smooth surface to form grooves. If the surface is smooth and the grooves are distinct, the concrete is ready to use *(left, below)*. If the surface roughens or the grooves are indistinct, add more cement and water, using twice as much cement as water. If the surface is wet or the grooves collapse, add sand and coarse aggregate combined in the original proportions. Re-test the batch until the consistency is correct.

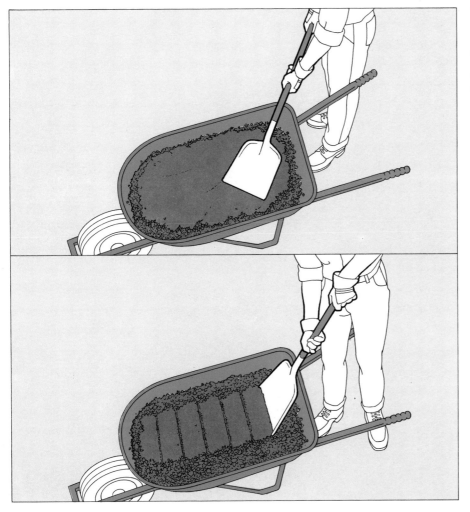

Solid Bases for Posts and Poles

The strongest way to set a post in the ground is to anchor it in concrete. Thus secured, fences will stand straight longer, rotary clothes driers and flagpoles will resist toppling, and playground equipment will become stable and safe to play on. A concrete anchorage is by far the safest installation for a climbing frame.

Every post-setting job begins with a hole. A manual post-hole borer, which looks like two shovels hinged together like pincers (*right*), can produce holes 150 mm in diameter or larger and up to a metre deep. A borer can be hired from tool hire companies and some fence manufacturers. If you need to dig several holes, you may want to hire a petrol-powered auger. If you have only one or two posts to secure, dig the holes manually with a spade.

Manufacturers of fencing and other outdoor equipment usually suggest how big a hole to dig. The hole should be deep enough to encase about a quarter of the length of the post (but no more than a metre). The width of the hole should allow enough clearance all round the post for pouring concrete. If the hole does not extend below the frost line, taper the hole to widen the bottom 25 to 50 mm to a bell shape (*right*), so that frost is less likely to heave the post.

To keep wooden posts from rotting, soak them overnight in one or another of the commercially available standard preservatives. Coat the buried ends of aluminium and steel with bituminous paint to prevent corrosion. Then simply pour concrete round the posts—except in the case of flagpoles or rotary clothes driers. They usually come with a metal sleeve that is anchored for the pole itself to slip into (and out of). For a long two or three section pole that would be awkward to lift out of its sleeve, a third anchoring alternative is a hinge support (*overleaf*).

For any of these anchoring methods, use the recipe for foundation concrete on page 26. How much concrete to mix depends on the size of the hole. A 150 mm hole holds roughly 0.002 cubic metres of concrete for each 100 mm of its depth, a 200 mm hole takes 0.004 cubic metres for each 100 mm of depth and a 300 mm hole, 0.008 cubic metres for each 100 mm of depth. For a single post, use dry-mix concrete.

Setting Fence Posts

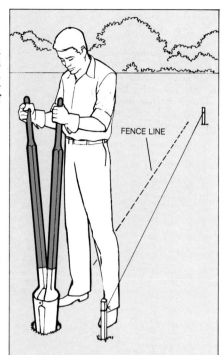

1 **Digging the holes.** Tie a string guide between stakes set about 300 mm outside the ends and corners. With a post-hole borer or a power auger, dig holes at the intervals specified for your fencing. Place 150 mm of gravel in the bottom of each hole for drainage.

FENCE LINE

2 **Centring a post.** To align a wooden post, set two stakes next to the hole and fasten a sturdy wooden brace to each stake with a single nail. Set the post in the hole, get it vertical with a level and nail the braces to the post. If you are installing a metal or concrete post, omit this stage, but have a helper ready to hold the post in position during the next operation.

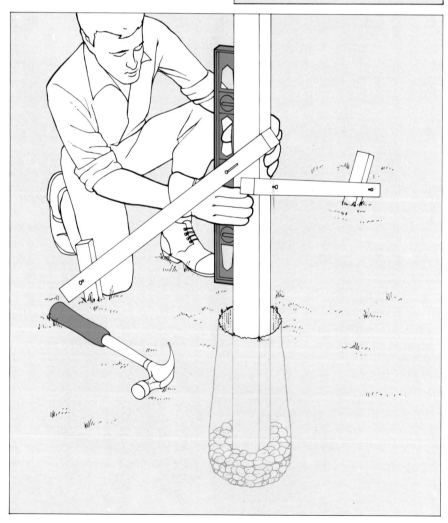

3 **Pouring the concrete.** For a braced wooden pole, simply fill the hole round the post with concrete, overfilling the hole slightly. For a metal or concrete post, ask a helper to hold it centred in the hole while you pour the concrete. Then hold a level alongside the post to align it. Attach guy ropes to hold it in position.

4 **Finishing the concrete.** Compact the concrete firmly with a length of timber. When standing water has evaporated from the concrete, bevel the surface downwards with a trowel so that rainwater will run away from the post. Cover the concrete with some soil to keep it moist while it cures. Wait a day before removing the braces or guy ropes, and a week before attaching any fencing. If the concrete pulls away from the post, pour some grout into the gap.

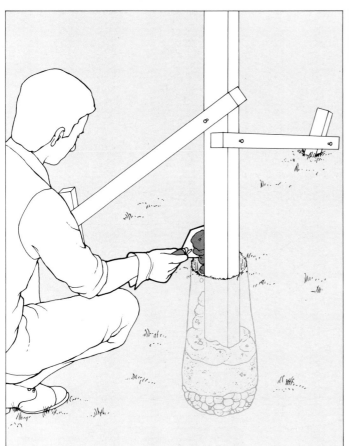

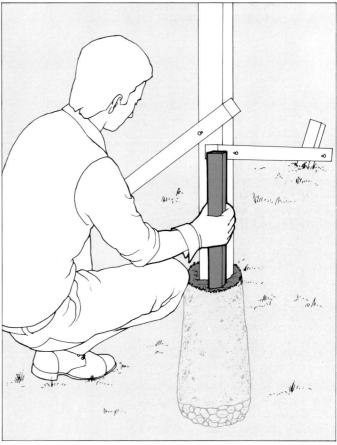

A Sleeve for a Temporary Pole

By anchoring a short metal sleeve in the ground, you will be able to slip a pole into the anchor and remove or rotate it at will. The procedure for installing a sleeve is basically the same as for setting a permanent post, although a sleeve will require a slightly larger hole to enable it to resist, for example, the sideways pull of an unevenly loaded rotary clothes drier.

Dig a hole about 100 mm deeper than the length of the sleeve. Spread 150 mm of gravel at the bottom of the hole so that the sleeve will extend about 50 mm above the ground when installed. Hold the sleeve centred in the hole. Fill the hole with concrete, overfilling it slightly. If the sleeve shifts, re-centre it and align it vertically before the concrete sets.

You can judge by eye if a sleeve for a short pole is vertical, but sleeves for tall poles may require precise alignment. To do this, wedge a length of wood into the sleeve and align the wood vertically with a level. Leave the wood in place until the concrete has hardened. Finish the concrete as for a permanent post *(above)*.

A Hinge for a Tall Pole

1 **Making the hinge.** Raising and lowering a tall, multisection pole is easier if it pivots on a pair of steel supports made from two lengths of 75 mm wide and 10 mm thick channel iron, each one-fifth the total length of the pole. A steel stockist will be able to provide the channel iron and can drill 20 mm holes in the positions indicated on the right. Take the pole with you and have it drilled at the same time. Assemble the hinge by bolting the channel irons and bottom pole section together with 16 mm galvanized bolts (*right*).

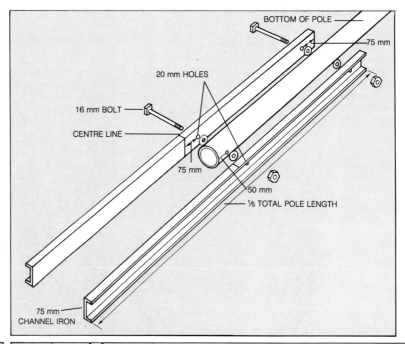

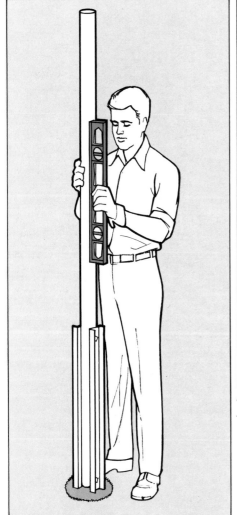

2 **Setting the hinge.** Dig a hole 500 mm in diameter and 150 mm deeper than half the length of the channel irons. Spread 150 mm of gravel in the hole, then fill it with concrete. With the hinge attached to the pole bottom, push the lower halves of the channel irons into the concrete, holding a level against the pole to align it. Check that the concrete is firmly packed round the channel irons and bevel its surface downwards. Leave the pole section bolted to the hinge while the concrete sets.

3 **Raising the pole.** Once the concrete has cured and hardened for several days, remove the bottom pole section from the hinge and assemble the pole; then bolt the pole to the channel irons through the top set of holes. Station a helper at the base of the channel irons and raise the pole so that he can insert the second bolt.

Stabilizing a Climbing Frame

1 **Preparing the holes.** Assemble the climbing frame and drive a stake into the ground at each leg. Position the stakes on the same side of each leg. Move the frame aside, then dig a hole centred on each stake, at least 450 mm deep and wide enough to allow room for both the frame legs and an anchorage of concrete.

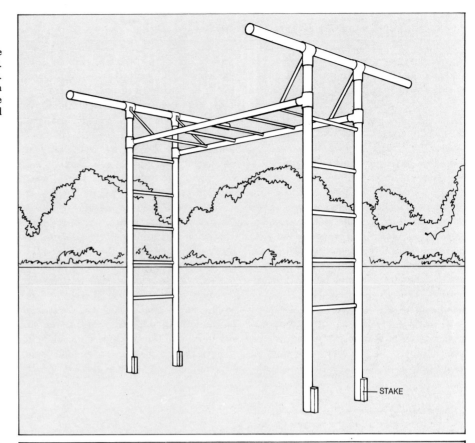

2 **Pouring the concrete.** Spread 150 mm of gravel in the bottom of each hole, then set the frame into the holes. Level the frame by adding or subtracting gravel, and fill the holes with concrete. Bevel the top of the concrete away from the legs. Caution: do not permit the frame to be used until the concrete has cured for a couple of weeks.

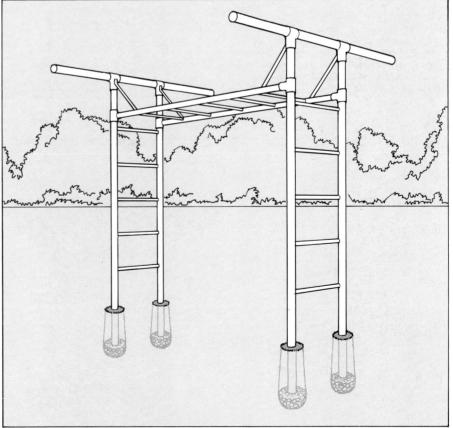

Making Holes and Securing Fixings

Many home improvement projects, such as erecting railings, installing outdoor wiring or running a pipe to an outside tap, require holes in walls or steps, special supports, or both. The holes are easy to make, but you must wear goggles. Various fixings are designed for this job—wallplugs, anchors, spring or gravity toggles, adhesive fillers and even nails shot out of a gun.

Most fixings fit into pre-drilled holes. Small holes in lightweight concrete blocks and plaster can be made with a carbide-tipped masonry bit in a rotary-action electric drill. For holes larger than 20 mm, use a four-edged chisel called a star drill.

For holes up to 10 mm across in dense blocks, concrete, brick or stone, use a hammer drill with a special bit, also tipped with carbide. Hammer drills are constructed so that they pound the bit into the masonry over 10,000 times per minute, giving the tip a sharp bite. Many rotary-action drills incorporate an optional hammer mechanism; when using one, start the hole with rotary drilling and then switch to the hammer action to finish the job. For holes between 10 and 25 mm, you will have to hire a heavy-duty industrial hammer drill. Holes larger than 25 mm are most easily made by using a masonry core bit—similar to a hole saw for wood—which can only be used in a rotary drill *(opposite)*.

Which fixing you use depends partly on the object you are mounting, partly on the wall. For most purposes, wallplugs, anchors and toggles of the kind used in interior plaster and plasterboard will do the job. Screws driven into wallplugs or anchors are suitable for concrete and the solid parts of blocks. They can be used in mortar joints and in brick if you are careful not to tighten the screw so much that the material round the edge of the hole begins to crumble. Toggles are needed for the hollow parts of the blocks.

In stone, wallplugs and anchors are unsatisfactory; they can create stresses that will cause cracks. For this material—and any solid structure where a very strong fixing is required—a technique employed in road construction to anchor concrete slabs is useful. A stud is made from an ordinary galvanized bolt by securing the head in a hole with epoxy, and the object is secured to the bolt with a nut.

Masonry nails can be driven by hand into lightweight blocks and the mortar joints between bricks or dense blocks, but are best reserved for attaching light loads such as battens for panelling. To drive masonry nails into concrete, stone or brick, use a special tool *(page 36)*.

Many different types of adhesives are available—choose one that is recommended for your purposes and follow the manufacturer's instructions.

Locating holes in bricks and concrete. Accurate marking for holes in bricks or concrete are especially important since drilling errors are virtually impossible to correct. Carefully check measurements and, wherever possible, use the object you are securing, such as the flanges for a railing, as a template. Get a helper to position awkward objects for marking and mark each hole with a centre punch so that the drill will not wander. Fasten one section at a time, so that errors do not accumulate.

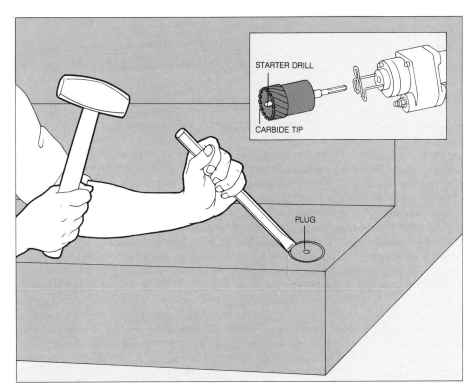

Drilling with a core bit. This carbide-tipped bit *(inset)*, which is used in a rotary drill, makes a hole by cutting a plug of concrete. The plug comes loose by itself if you drill clear through a structure, but if you bore only part of the way you must dislodge the plug with a cold chisel. Caution: wear goggles, hold the chisel against the edge of the plug and strike it with a club hammer. If the plug does not break off cleanly at the bottom of the hole, chisel out the rest and flush away debris with a hose-pipe.

Studs Made from Bolts

1 Setting a bolt in epoxy. Mark and drill holes for the studs, then dust off the brickwork near the holes. Cut a strip of masking tape for each stud, and with a trimming knife slice an X in the centre of each strip to make an opening for the threaded ends of the bolts. Insert a bolt head-first into a hole and, with a filling knife, fill the space round the bolt with epoxy. Stick a piece of tape firmly to the wall, with the bolt projecting through the X; the tape keeps the bolt centred in the hole and the epoxy from oozing out. Repeat the procedure for the other bolts and allow the epoxy to cure for the length of time specified by the manufacturers before proceeding.

2 Marking stud holes in a strip of wood. Hold a level against the edge of the board you are mounting and push it against the studs. Plumb the board with the level—or level the board if it runs horizontally—then strike it sharply with a rubber mallet, opposite the studs, to make indented guide marks. Drill holes centred on these imprints and fasten the board to the studs with washers and nuts.

A Gun for Driving Nails

Hardened-steel masonry nails are often used to fasten battens to walls for panelling or shelves and to anchor wall framing to a concrete floor. A fast and easy way to do this is with a tool called a low-velocity cartridge gun or hammer, which employs the explosive force of a blank cartridge to force a nail or rivet into mortar, block, concrete or steel. The cartridge hammer will not fire unless it is pressed firmly against a wall or floor. When used correctly, it is safe, has virtually no recoil and makes very little noise. To make certain that its operation is understood, agencies that supply the cartridge hammer usually show their customers precisely how to use the gun before they hire it out.

Blank cartridges for the cartridge hammer come with a variety of charges, or loads. A smaller charge is needed to drive a nail into mortar, for example, than into concrete, a much harder material. Cartridge hammers require special nails and rivets which are usually supplied with the gun. (Do not strike them with an ordinary hammer; they may shatter into sharp pieces.) Choose a nail that is long enough to pass through the board you are nailing and about 20 mm into the masonry; deeper or shallower penetration weakens the fixing. For safety, keep the cartridge hammer, nails and cartridges out of children's reach.

1 Loading the nail. To avoid accidents, wear goggles when firing a cartridge hammer and follow exactly these instructions for using it. First, hold the tool in one hand and with the other drop a nail head-first down the barrel. Then, using the ramrod supplied with the gun, push the nail into the barrel as far as it will go. The spacer near the point of the nail centres it in the barrel and reinforces the head once you have driven the nail into place.

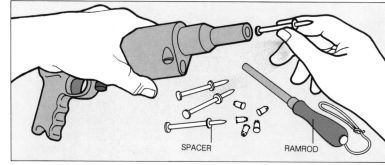

SPACER   RAMROD

2 Loading the blank cartridge. Open the cartridge hammer, slip the blank into the firing chamber and then close the gun. On the model illustrated here, the tool is opened by depressing the button near the trigger guard and twisting the two halves of the assembly apart.

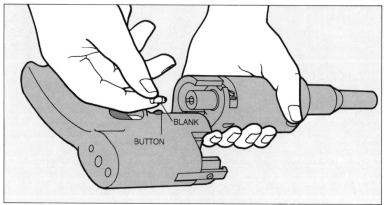

BLANK

BUTTON

3 Firing the driver. Push the barrel of the gun against the material you are fastening—in this case, a batten. The barrel will slide into the driver about 25 mm, releasing the trigger safety catch. Keeping up the pressure, hold the driver at a right angle to the wall and squeeze the trigger. The gun will fire, countersinking the nail. If the nail head protrudes from the board, re-load the empty gun with a lighter charge and fire again to seat the nail firmly, then switch to a heavier powder charge for the next nail; alternatively, if the first nail is countersunk too deeply, switch to a lighter charge.

COUNTERSUNK NAIL

Cleaning Up After the Work Is Done

Cleaning up after any masonry job usually consists of at least two different tasks: disposing of mortar or concrete that remains unused at the end of the job, and then cleaning your tools.

Leftover concrete or mortar can be a nuisance, for most refuse departments will not remove such waste. Generally you have to take it yourself to the nearest dump. For easier handling, pour it into paper bags, or pile it in small heaps on sheets of paper and let it set into manageable lumps. Or you can mould concrete and save it for future use—some householders, for example, keep simple wooden forms ready for pouring excess concrete

into while it is still workable, and cast their own paving slabs.

Cleaning tools is an ongoing task that should be done as you work. Scrub off small patches of hardened concrete or mortar with a wire brush and a scraper, or a piece of brick or block, as soon as they appear. At the end of the day, put all your tools in a wheelbarrow or bucket, and hose them down together. Let the sediment settle and pour the clear water away. Dispose of the sediment as you would excess mortar or concrete. When the entire job is finished, coat all steel tools with petroleum jelly to prevent them from rusting.

A power concrete mixer must be hosed out at the end of each working day. (Many hire companies will charge an extra fee for a mixer that is returned dirty.) If you cannot clean the drum completely with a hose-pipe, turn the mixer on and pour in a mixture of water and two shovelfuls of coarse aggregate to scour it out. Empty the mixer after 10 minutes, then hose it out again. If you have waited too long to clean the mixer, you may find that you still have to scrape bits of hardened concrete out with a wire brush or chip them out with a chisel. A dull-grey exterior film of dry cement should be sponged off with vinegar.

Removing Stains and Blemishes

Scrubbing with water gets most blemishes off masonry, but some stains may need to be treated with household cleansers or chemicals from chemists or specialist suppliers. Caution: many of these substances are hazardous and corrosive. Keep them away from children, follow dilution instructions, wear protective clothing, and provide ample ventilation. Remove all traces of the cleanser by rinsing with water after treatment.

Concrete and Brick
□ EFFLORESCENCE (a white, powdery deposit produced when internal moisture dissolves the salts in bricks and concrete). Rub the deposit with a bristle brush and mop with a damp sponge.
□ OIL AND GREASE. Scrub with a strong solution of household washing soda, a proprietary emulsifying agent (available from car accessory shops), or a smooth, stiff paste made from talc and either petrol or benzene. (The talc helps to keep the mixture in place.) Wipe or rinse off, adding detergent to the water to remove cleansers based on petrol, benzene or emulsifying agent. These stains can be difficult to remove, especially if they have soaked below the surface.

□ TAR AND BITUMEN. First chill the material with ice to make it brittle, then chip away as much of the deposit as possible. Apply a paste of talc and petrol or benzene. A faint brown blemish may remain even after repeated applications.
□ PAINT AND VARNISH. Apply a proprietary paint remover to oil-based paints. Leave for the time recommended and then scrape off. Acetone, benzene or methylated spirits should remove emulsion paint, shellac or varnish. All types of paint are difficult to remove, however, and large areas, or paint lodged in the cracks of rough-textured brick, may have to be removed professionally.
□ RUST. Scrub with a stiff brush and a solution of 1 part citric acid crystals dissolved in 7 parts of water containing washing-up liquid. Stubborn rust marks should be lightly etched with a solution of 1 part hydrochloric acid—sometimes called spirit of salts—to 20 parts water for a few moments. In either case, rinse thoroughly with fresh water as soon as the stain has disappeared. Caution: rust stains in concrete that follow the pattern of steel reinforcement may indicate corrosion of the steel, which will cause spalling if not treated professionally.

□ ORGANIC GROWTHS. Fungi, algae and mosses can be killed by spraying on a proprietary fungicide, which will leave a toxic residue to prevent new growths.
□ BEVERAGE AND INK STAINS. Scrub with household bleach and rinse with clear water.
□ SMOKE AND ATMOSPHERIC POLLUTANTS. Scrub with kitchen and bathroom cleanser. Rinse thoroughly.
□ BROWN STAIN (caused by the manganese used to colour dark brick). Wet the brick and brush with a solution of 1 part acetic acid, 1 part hydrogen peroxide and 6 parts water. Rinse thoroughly.
□ MORTAR SMEARS. Try to avoid these during construction. If cleaning is necessary, use a proprietary mortar remover, or apply a solution of 1 part hydrochloric acid to 20 parts water with a fibre or plastic brush—do not use a bristle or wire brush. Rinse thoroughly.

Stone
Remove minor stains on granite and slate with washing-up liquid, and rinse thoroughly. Use only clear water on limestone or sandstone and do not scrub them too vigorously. Heavy staining must be treated professionally.

2

The Magnificent Mud

Creating a smooth surface. A steel float is swept lightly over newly poured concrete, leaving a silky finish. Used when the sheen of surface water has disappeared, the float eliminates all irregularities. A rougher finish can be produced by brushing the concrete with a stiff broom.

Concrete is a misunderstood material. A wet paste when poured, it solidifies into one of the most durable of all building materials. Prosaic as mud (from which it was originally made), it has inspired outstanding architects to create plastic fantasies—half sculpture, half structure. For the amateur, it is no less versatile. It can be moulded into any shape ranging from a slab to a cylinder, or from steps to a bird-bath. And once understood, its techniques are easily mastered.

Concrete nearly always requires forms, and sometimes reinforcement as well. Forms are generally bottomless wooden boxes into which freshly mixed concrete is poured and held until a complex chemical reaction takes place among its ingredients to harden it into man-made stone. Although most forms are temporary installations, planning and building them can be the most time-consuming aspect of concrete work. For some jobs—like the steps on pages 66–67—you will need less than half an hour to pour the concrete; but you have to be prepared to spend a day or two constructing and positioning the necessary forms.

If forms guarantee that your concrete follows a desired outline, reinforcement may be needed to ensure that your finished structure holds together. One major shortcoming of concrete is its comparatively low tensile strength—although it supports great weight pressing against it, it is relatively easily pulled apart. Reinforcement remedies this lack. In small slabs for paths, control and expansion joints obviate the need for reinforcement. The joints channel the stresses caused by expansion and contraction, as well as by concrete's natural shrinkage after pouring, so that cracking occurs where it causes the least damage. But for very large slabs or thick blocks, it is necessary to add steel reinforcement in the form of heavy wire mesh. Because concrete begins to harden quickly, careful planning is essential to attain a satisfactory finish. During the crucial hour or two after mixing, work rapidly so that the concrete does not become unworkable before you have completed the several smoothing operations required. If you want to pour a large project, such as a drive or a patio, all in one swoop, you will need helpers. But you can handle it alone, at your own pace, if you divide it up into small sections, as described on page 61.

Whether you assemble a task force or work by yourself, there is no need to settle for utilitarian drabness. The structure will be practical and durable if you simply follow the recipes. Attractive it can also be if you apply your own imagination. A path, for instance, need not be a dull grey series of rectangles; it can be shaped to any pattern, given colour with pigment, or texture with stones pressed into its surface. You can do the same with steps, a drive or a patio, for the plasticity of concrete makes it the most versatile of masonry materials.

Building with Concrete: the Preliminaries

Almost any concrete work you undertake—even a patio tucked into a corner of your garden—may run up against building or planning regulations or even restrictions in the fine print of your mortgage or the title deeds of your house. Before you start, check with local authorities who will be able to advise you on the necessary procedures. Many building codes and planning regulations dictate the dimensions, location and design you can have, and the standards that the materials and techniques you use must meet. You may need to obtain a building permit.

Rarely do these technicalities place any unreasonable burden on you; in fact, they can often help you by preventing mistakes. In addition, you must contend with nature and geography: the character of the site where you want your project to go. Take into account the slope of the terrain, the trees, shrubs and their roots, any rock outcrop, the location of gas, electric, water or sewage lines and of any soakaways, septic tanks, cesspools or oil storage tanks—including abandoned ones. Measure the distances that will be important in planning your project. Then draw a scale layout that shows existing structures and landscape features.

At the site, dig a test hole about 300 mm deep to check the soil. Concrete paving and a footing for a garden wall do not need to extend below the frost line as house foundations do, but they require excavations deep enough to reach firm ground or provide space for a sub-base of crushed stone or hoggin (a mixture of clayey sand and gravel) under the concrete. If your soil is firm and sandy, you will not need to lay a sub-base for a path or patio. A 100 mm thick sub-base will be necessary under a drive or if the soil is clayey or peaty. The sub-base allows the concrete to shift without cracking, if the earth heaves with changing weather.

Whatever the soil, the ground must be stable. Avoid any site with more than a metre of recent landfill, which might settle. If you strike water in the test hole, the job will require professional skills.

After you make your test to decide how deep the excavation should be, you can clear the area by moving plants that might be in the way and, if necessary, getting rid of old concrete. To break up concrete that is not reinforced with wire mesh, lift and drop a heavy sledge hammer—do not try to swing it—working from the edges towards the centre. For reinforced concrete, call in a professional. If you live in a cold climate, you can break unreinforced concrete during the winter by drilling 40 mm deep holes into it at 300 mm intervals with a masonry bit. Fill the holes with water during a cold spell; the water will freeze and burst the concrete. An old path will break if you lift up an edge with a crowbar, slide a rock underneath and then pull out the bar so that the slab falls down on the rock. Dispose of the concrete chunks by hiring a hauler to come and remove them.

With the site cleared, check your preliminary drawings by using garden hose or string to lay out the path or other project in the place where you plan to build it. Then, on the basis of the new measurements, you can decide whether to make your own concrete (pages 26–29) or buy it ready-mixed (right). Since you will divide most slabs into segments to permit them to expand and contract as the temperature fluctuates, it is a simple matter to install home-mixed concrete one segment at a time, a procedure that permits you to prepare small batches yourself. For faster results, you may order large quantities delivered by a ready-mix truck.

Estimating how much concrete you need for the project, and how much crushed stone or hoggin a sub-base will require, takes only simple arithmetic. All three materials are sold by the cubic metre, so you must estimate the length, width and depth dimensions in advance. For slabs, footings and sub-bases use the table given below—which includes an extra allowance of 8 per cent for wastage—to work out the quantities required. For steps, multiply the length by the width by the depth to determine the total amount of cubic metres necessary.

Estimating Materials for Concrete Slabs

Area of slab	Thickness of slab 100 mm	150 mm	250 mm
1 sq metre	0.11 cu metres	0.16 cu metres	0.27 cu metres
2.5 sq metres	0.27 cu metres	0.4 cu metres	0.75 cu metres
5 sq metres	0.54 cu metres	0.81 cu metres	1.35 cu metres
10 sq metres	1.08 cu metres	1.62 cu metres	2.7 cu metres
20 sq metres	2.16 cu metres	3.24 cu metres	5.4 cu metres
30 sq metres	3.24 cu metres	4.86 cu metres	8.1 cu metres
40 sq metres	4.32 cu metres	6.48 cu metres	10.8 cu metres
50 sq metres	5.4 cu metres	8.1 cu metres	13.5 cu metres

Matching area, thickness and cubic metres. This table gives the number of cubic metres of concrete, crushed stone or hoggin required to make concrete slabs and the sub-bases beneath slabs up to 250 mm thick, with an 8 per cent allowance for waste and spillage. To use the table, first decide the thickness of the slab. A sub-base should always be 100 mm thick, but the thickness of a slab depends on the use for which it is intended. A slab on firm soil for a path or patio or for a drive that is intended only for cars need be only 100 mm thick; a slab on clayey soil or one that will be used by heavy vehicles requires a depth of 150 mm; and a footing for a garden wall should be at least 250 mm thick. Next, calculate the area in square metres. Look up the volume required by locating the horizontal column that lists an area closest to yours and going across to the vertical column for the thickness you need.

Coping with the Ready-Mix Truck

For large jobs you can save work by buying the concrete from a ready-mix supplier who will make it to your specifications and deliver it ready to be poured into place. But you will have to work fast and enlist several assistants.

Tell the supplier how many cubic metres you need and specify the type of mix you want. A knowledge of the supplier's jargon is helpful when ordering. In Britain, where the terminology adopted by the British Standards Institution (BSI) is used, general-purpose concrete is described as a "C20P mix to BS 5328" and foundation concrete as a "C7.5P mix to BS 5328". (C stands for compressive strength and the number indicates the strength the mix will attain; P means that the mix is prescribed by proportions rather than being specially designed for the job; while BS 5328 refers to the relevant British Standard specification.) Ask for the mix to have high workability and a 20 mm maximum aggregate size. The specifications of air-entrained paving concrete are not laid down by the BSI. To order it, request a special prescribed mix with a minimum cement content of 330 kg per cubic metre, 4 per cent entrained air, and a 100 mm target slump—a measure of the workability of concrete that refers to the amount a cone-shaped mass of concrete will slump when the conical form is lifted off.

Always ask for the mix to be retarded by two hours. This means that a retarding agent will be added to the mix, giving you up to four hours from the time of mixing (which may take place at the depot) to move, pour and finish the concrete before it becomes unworkable.

How much you pay for ready-mix depends on the size of your order. If you need more than about 5 cubic metres of concrete, you may find the mix costs less than buying materials and combining them yourself. If you need less, you may have to pay a delivery charge or a higher price per cubic metre. Most prices include 30 to 45 minutes' delivery time. When the truck spends longer than that unloading, you pay an hourly rate for the extra time.

To speed up delivery, decide in advance where the truck will stop and how you will get the concrete to the work site. The best plan is to have the truck discharge the concrete directly into the form work, but to do this it may have to drive on to your property, since the form work must be no more than 3 metres from the rear of the truck. This can cause problems—the weight of a truck can break a kerb, drive or path and make ruts a metre deep in a lawn.

If the time and work saved would be worth the risk, however, you can minimize the damage by laying 50 mm thick planks along the truck's route to equalize the load. Never let the truck drive over septic tanks or cesspools; it could crash through the ground. If the truck must park in the street, you will have to use wheelbarrows—manned by a platoon of helpers—to unload the concrete.

Unloading by wheelbarrow. Place a thick plywood panel where the truck will discharge the concrete. Then lay sturdy planks from the unloading area to your work site to make a firm surface for rolling loaded wheelbarrows—they may sink into a lawn. Make sure that you have sufficient helpers and wheelbarrows on hand. A single cubic metre of concrete weighs 2.4 tonnes and makes 25 to 30 wheelbarrow loads. When the truck arrives, work quickly with a shovel to slide the concrete from the delivery chute into a wheelbarrow. Take care not to overfill the wheelbarrow. And do not leave any concrete in the chute—it may drop out before someone can get a wheelbarrow positioned underneath.

Setting Up Forms for Slabs

Forms are moulds that shape concrete into slabs for paths, patios and drives, and footings for low walls. They are built like bottomless boxes. Boards or metal strips, set on edge, outline the outer edges of the concrete and may also divide a large area into smaller—and more workable—units. Except for forms made of rot-resistant or treated timber, which will remain in the slab as a permanent decorative feature *(page 61)*, forms are temporary constructions—assembled on the site before the concrete is poured and then removed after the concrete has cured.

Even for small jobs, forms have to be strong enough to withstand the weight of the concrete. Straight form sections for a simple 100 mm slab, such as a path *(right, below)* or patio, require timber which is 50 by 100 mm. Where you need to shape curved sections of concrete, forms can be made with strips of thin sheet metal.

Temporary forms are best made of straight-grained softwood which, unlike timber used in most construction, should be smooth and green. Fully dried wood may absorb moisture from the concrete and interfere with curing. To determine how much you need, measure the outer dimensions of the marked area *(opposite page, top)*. Continuous boards will make the strongest forms, but long sections may be made by nailing strips to the backs of abutting boards. Separate form boards may be necessary to make expansion joints within the slab *(page 49)*. A cheaper alternative to wooden forms is to hire steel forms—available in rigid and flexible 3 metre lengths—from a plant-hire agency.

In addition to these materials, you also need a generous supply of sturdy wooden stakes, each about 500 mm long. They are used first to mark the layout and then to support the forms and to brace them.

The support stakes also indicate the slope, or fall, of the slab that directs rainwater away from the nearest building. If you are laying a simple path that will run in a straight line over land that slopes gently away from the building, follow the slope of the land. The path will then be flush with the ground, and the stakes for forms are driven so that their tops are flush with the ground as well. If the ground is flat, or if the slab is large or complicated by angles and curves, the concrete must be set

to a fall for drainage as shown in detail on the following pages.

Forms are installed after you have laid out, excavated and levelled the area. A slab for a garden path or a patio can usually be laid directly on to firm, well-compacted soil. But a drive, or any slab laid on clay or peat soils, should rest on a 100 mm thick sub-base of crushed stone or hoggin. Caution: in the planning stage of any project that will abut an existing wall, check that the top of the finished slab will be at least 150 mm below the damp-proof course in the wall. A slab larger than 3 or 4 square metres should be broken up by expansion joints into smaller units. The joints allow the units to shift independently as frost heaves the ground—they float like rafts on a gentle sea—so that the slab will not be subjected to cracking stresses.

After the forms are assembled and set to a fall, the sub-base can be laid in place *(page 49)*. Large slabs—patios and drives—may need a layer of wire-mesh reinforcement *(pages 58–63)*, but small slabs for paths do not. After the bed has been levelled and the expansion joints set in place, the site will be ready for concrete.

The Simplest Slab

Building basic forms. A straight path on gently sloping ground requires only a little time and effort to lay out. After the path is outlined and the site excavated and levelled, support stakes are set at both ends—just far enough outside the proposed slab width to allow space for form boards—and at 1 metre intervals in between. Pound the tops of the stakes flush with ground level *(below)*. Nail the boards to the stakes, flush with the tops and suspended above the bottom of the excavation to provide for a 100 mm deep sub-base beneath the slab, if required. Bracing stakes, positioned diagonally, supply additional strength where the form boards are pieced together. If the site does not slope gently away from the nearest building, or if curves and turns are involved, the slab must be set to a fall as shown on the following pages.

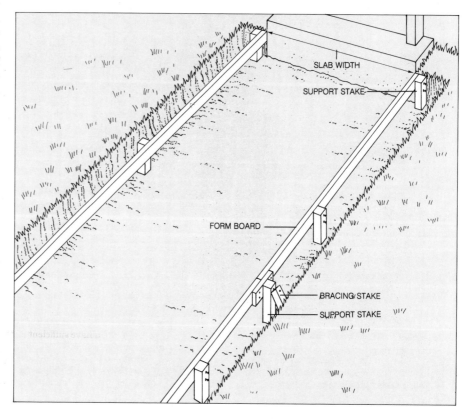

Excavating the Base

1 **Outlining the slab.** For a straight small slab, drive pairs of stakes on both sides of the proposed slab at the beginning and end of the site. Tie strings to the stakes. To mark the string line on the ground, take a handful of sand and let it trickle out over the strings to make a sand outline. For a curved slab, drive additional stakes at intervals of between 300 mm and 1 metre—the sharper the curve, the closer the stakes should be round each curve. Run the strings for both sides round these stakes. For a forked path, drive stakes round curves and at the beginning and end of each straight section before attaching strings.

2 **Preparing the ground.** After removing marker stakes and strings, dig a trench of the required depth 300 mm outside one sand line. If a sub-base is necessary—as in the path shown here—make the excavation 100 mm deeper than the depth of the concrete in the finished slab. Be careful to remove all vegetable matter, but save the turf if you want to replace it along the edge of the slab. Then, digging from inside the slab area, complete the excavation, extending the trench 300 mm beyond the opposite sand line.

3 **Levelling the ground.** Smooth the excavation with a rake and fill in with sand or gravel any soft spots or holes left by the removal of large stones. Flatten and level the earth by pulling a board across the surface. For a path or narrow slab, use a board as long as the excavation is wide.

4 **Tamping the ground.** Compact the bottom of the excavation with a lawn roller, a spare tyre *(page 69)*, or a tamper made by nailing and bracing a sturdy piece of wood about 1 metre long to a board 300 to 350 mm square. Nail door handles at the top, one on each side. Fill and tamp low spots. Then use the levelling board *(Step 3)* as a straightedge to be sure the trench bottom is fairly even across its entire width.

Staking the Site

Driving support stakes. For a straight, small slab, restake the ends within the excavated base. Set the stakes outside the desired slab width by exactly the thickness of the form boards you will be using. Drive the stakes at least 300 mm deep. Run strings along the inner faces of each set of stakes. Then drive intermediate support stakes at 1 metre intervals along both sides of the slab and at the joints of boards, positioning the inner faces of the stakes against the strings.

For a curve, or fork, drive extra pairs of stakes at the ends of each additional straight section before attaching the strings. Do not set stakes round curves at this point.

On a smoothly sloping site, slope the slab by pounding down each support stake until the top is at ground level. Then skip the instructions below and overleaf, and proceed to setting up the form boards (*page 47*). If the ground slopes unevenly, set the stakes to a fall by following the instructions below.

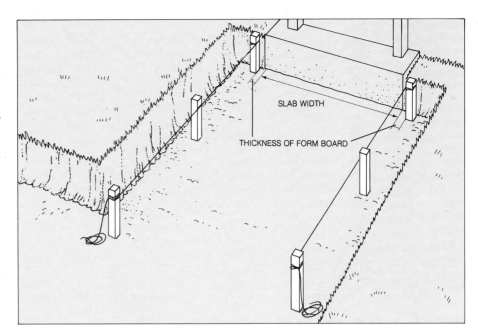

SLAB WIDTH

THICKNESS OF FORM BOARD

Setting the Stakes to a Fall

FALL LINE

1 **Setting the lengthwise slope.** For a straight slab on perfectly flat ground, use a waterproof marker to draw a line at ground level on the inner face of one of the support stakes nearest the building. Continue the line round the side of the stake away from the building. Then use a level to make a mark at the same height on the adjacent stake. To slope the slab and ensure that rainwater does not collect near the building, draw a fall line 10 mm below the mark. Use the level to mark a fall line at this height on each of the adjacent support stakes along one side of the slab. For a forked path, like the one illustrated, treat one fork as the main section for setting the slab to a fall.

2 **Finishing the lengthwise slope.** Set a long board across the width of the slab in front of the stakes nearest the building. Position the top edge of the board under the line on the marked stake and drive one double-headed nail to hold the board temporarily in place. Then level the board and mark a line on the opposite stake. Remove the board. Indicate the lengthwise slope for the forms by drawing a 10 mm lower line on the adjacent stake, following the method in Step 1.

3 **Setting widthwise slope on flat ground.** At the far end of a straight slab or the main section of a forked path, align a board with the fall line on the last stake on the marked side. Drive in one nail to hold the board. Use a level and the board to mark the opposite stake. Remove the board and draw a fall line on this second stake below the mark, allowing 2.5 mm for every 100 mm of slab width. Fasten string from this fall line to the fall line on the second stake from the building. Mark the stakes where the string crosses the inner faces. Remove the string.

4 **Finishing the slope for a fork.** Slope the remaining fork widthwise only. Use the level to mark the stakes along the side nearest the building at the same height as the mark on the stake at the inner juncture of the fork. Slope the opposite side by running a string line from the end stake to the stake at the outer juncture of the fork, sloping it so that it is lower at the end of the section than at the beginning. Allow a gradient of 2.5 mm for each 100 mm of slab width.

Nailing on the Form Boards

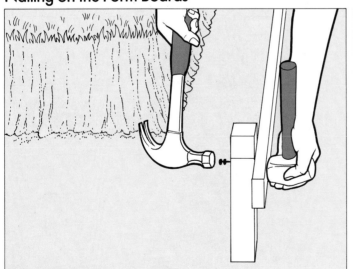

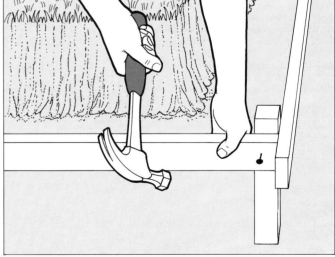

1 **Attaching form boards.** For a slab on sloping ground, drive a double-headed nail into a stake near the building, just below the top of the outer face. Lift one end of a form board level with the top, and drive the nail into it, using a club hammer to cushion the blows. Attach the board to the stake at the other end, then at the centre. Add a second set of nails below the first set. Finally, attach the board to the intermediate stakes. For a slab on a flat site, position the top edge of the board flush with the stake's fall lines.

2 **Making corners.** Butt the end of the corner form board against the back of the board for the straight section. Then use a single-headed nail to fasten the corner board to the face of the support stake, checking to be sure that the top edges of both form boards are level.

3 **Adding braces.** Drive a bracing stake angled from the form top into the excavation outside the support stakes at each corner. Where boards are pieced together, drive a perpendicular support stake before putting in a diagonal brace. Nail braces to support stakes below existing nails.

4 **Trimming forms.** For a forked path, saw off the ends of form boards where they overlap corners. Trim the tops of support stakes that project above form boards—except the pairs of stakes on the ends of curves—to provide a uniform flat surface for striking off the slab later.

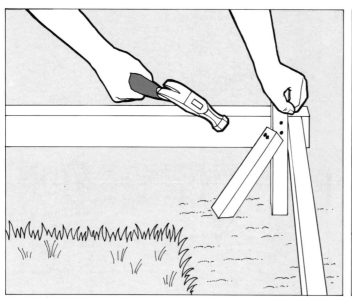

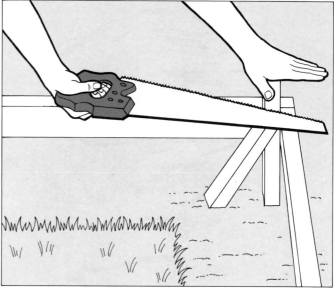

Shaping Curves with Metal

1 **Staking curves.** Arrange string in the desired arc round a curved section of the slab. To align the face of a 2 mm thick strip of sheet metal for the curve with the face of the form boards, begin and end the arc inside the adjacent form-board stakes by exactly the thickness of the form boards. Drive support stakes for the curve along the string line at intervals of between 300 mm and 1 metre, depending on the sharpness of the curve. To slope the curve for a slab on flat ground, run the string from the top of one form-board stake to the other across the faces of the stakes. Level the string with the tops of the adjacent form boards and pull it taut. Mark fall lines where the string crosses each stake. Remove the string.

2 **Attaching curved forms.** Cut a strip of sheet metal as wide as the form boards and about 150 mm longer than the curve. Attach the strip to the form board at one end of the curve with galvanized nails, overlapping the board by about 75 mm and aligning the top of the strip with the top edge of the board. Continue nailing round the curve to the form board at the opposite end. Add diagonal bracing stakes at each support stake, then saw off the tops of projecting support stakes level with the boards and metal strip. Backfill the trench outside the curve with earth for extra support, but be careful not to tamp the earth so hard that you move the stakes.

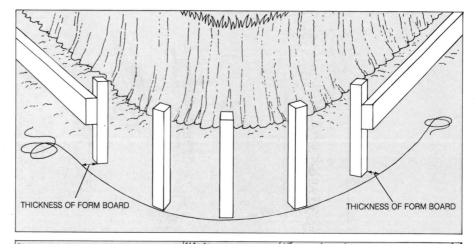

THICKNESS OF FORM BOARD   THICKNESS OF FORM BOARD

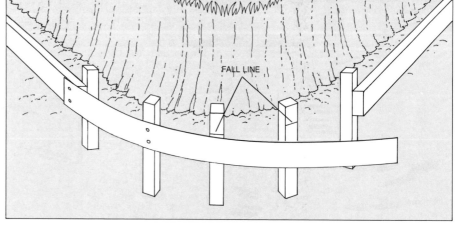

FALL LINE

Installing a Sub-Base

Placing the sub-base. Place a 100 mm deep layer of crushed stone or hoggin inside the forms if a sub-base is required. To level the material even with the bottom of the form boards, pull a levelling board—a sturdy length of wood placed on edge—towards you across the surface. Make the board the width of the space between the form boards and attach a wider length of wood to the top so that you rest the projecting ends on the forms as you pull the board. Fill in low places with the crushed stone or hoggin as you go. Use the tamper *(page 44, Step 4)* to compact the bed, adding more material if necessary. Then level the surface again with the board.

Expansion Joints

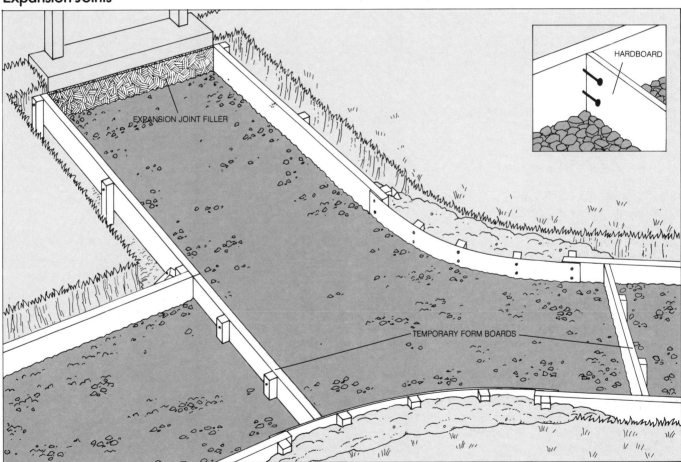

EXPANSION JOINT FILLER

HARDBOARD

TEMPORARY FORM BOARDS

Installing expansion joints. To allow for heat-caused expansion and contraction in a slab, joints are needed wherever the slab abuts an existing rigid structure, such as a step, wall or other slab. Cut pieces of 100 mm wide compressible expansion joint filler—usually bituminized felt—to the width of the slab, and place them between the slab and any abutting structure. (The semi-rigid material will stay in position by itself.) Within the slab, expansion joints are needed at intervals of no more than 4 metres or twice the width of the slab, whichever is less. Divide a slab more than 4 metres wide into equal-sized sections in both directions. The width and length of each section should not exceed 3 metres. If you plan to pour the concrete one section at a time, place a temporary form board across the slab wherever a joint is needed. Support it at right angles to the outer forms by staking from the outside. Pour the concrete into the slab section and allow it to cure for one to two days before removing the temporary form board and pouring concrete in the next section. The natural shrinkage of the concrete will open the joint sufficiently to allow for later heat-caused expansion. If you plan to pour all the concrete at once, use strips of hardboard to form the joints. Support the hardboard at both ends by driving pairs of galvanized nails half way into the form boards at the front and back of the board *(inset)*. When you pour the concrete, mound some on each side of the hardboard to keep it upright while you fill the forms. Leave the hardboard in place permanently.

Pouring and Finishing

Speed is the most important requirement for placing concrete into forms. A fresh mix needs to be poured and finished in under three hours; after that it is too hard to be workable. In that time, one man, working alone with ready-mix concrete, can place and finish about 9 metres of a 1 metre wide path like the one shown here. One assistant will allow him to finish 15 metres of path in the same time; two assistants, 20 metres.

As soon as concrete is poured into place (right, below), it must be compacted and levelled so that it is flush with the tops of the forms. This is done first with a spade, next with a tamping beam—a long board that is moved along the surface with an up-and-down motion—and then with a float-like darby. Compacting the concrete forces water to the surface. When this bleed water appears, all work must stop. Darbying or floating before this film of water has completely evaporated can make the slab crumble later. Air-entrained concrete bleeds relatively little, but it still may need 10 to 20 minutes before the water will evaporate completely on a hot, dry day—and an hour or more may be needed when the weather is cool or humid.

Once the sheen of this surface water disappears, the surface of the concrete must be finished and the edges rounded to reduce the chances of chipping at a later stage. For a slab you must also incise control joints into the surface every 1 to 1½ metres to induce cracks at the joints rather than at random. If you want the marks of the edging tool to remain, finish the surface with the desired texture first. Otherwise, round the edges before finishing.

Concrete can be coloured by mixing pigment into the entire batch. It can also be coloured during the last step by applying a layer of coloured mortar about 25 mm thick to the top of a normal concrete base. And, of course, it can be coloured with a coat of paint or stain, providing you leave the concrete to cure for six weeks and use specially formulated concrete coatings.

If you choose a mortar coat of colour, pour unpigmented concrete up to 25 mm below the top of the forms and tamp it level. As soon as the concrete begins to dry, apply the batch of coloured mortar and tamp it level with the top of the forms. Caution: use sharp concreting sand in the mortar rather than soft bricklaying sand.

Any desired finish except the smoothest may be applied to the surface of pre-coloured concrete; a grooved or flagstone texture can be given to mortar-coated concrete. Use only wooden finishing tools; a metal tool may discolour the surface.

Concrete must be kept damp and left undisturbed to cure for three to 10 days, depending on weather conditions, so that the chemical reactions that give it strength can proceed uninterrupted. After curing, the form boards can be removed, but heavy loads should still be kept off the concrete for at least another week.

New concrete must also be protected from freezing. Avoid pouring concrete in winter, and if the temperature falls unexpectedly, insulate fresh concrete by placing a "quilt" of straw between two layers of polythene or by laying earth, sand or compost over the sheeting.

Placing the Concrete

1 **Filling the forms.** Hose the forms and the sub-base thoroughly, but leave no puddles. Dump the first wheelbarrow load of concrete into the forms—those farthest from the lorry if you are using ready-mix. Then pack each successive load up against the preceding one, overfilling the forms by 10 to 15 mm. Be careful not to knock down or cover up the expansion joints within the slab. If you do not use temporary form boards to make expansion joints within the slab, as shown here for section-by-section pouring, mound wet concrete on either side of each strip of hardboard. If you plan to add a topping of coloured mortar, fill the forms only to within 25 mm of the tops. As you go, shovel the concrete into the corners of the forms, and jam the shovel edge through the concrete to eliminate all air pockets.

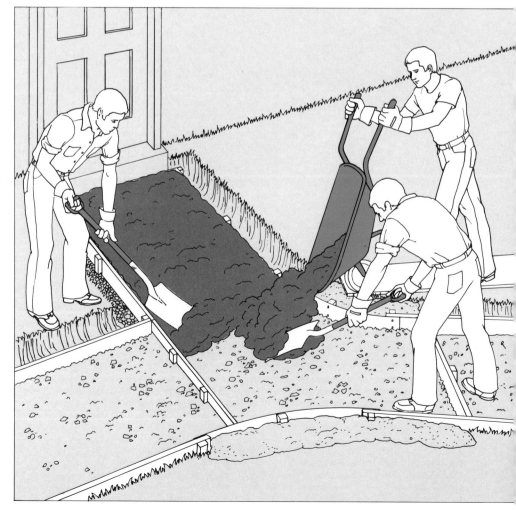

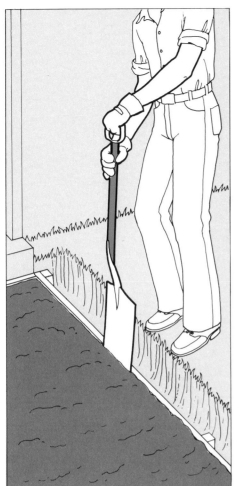

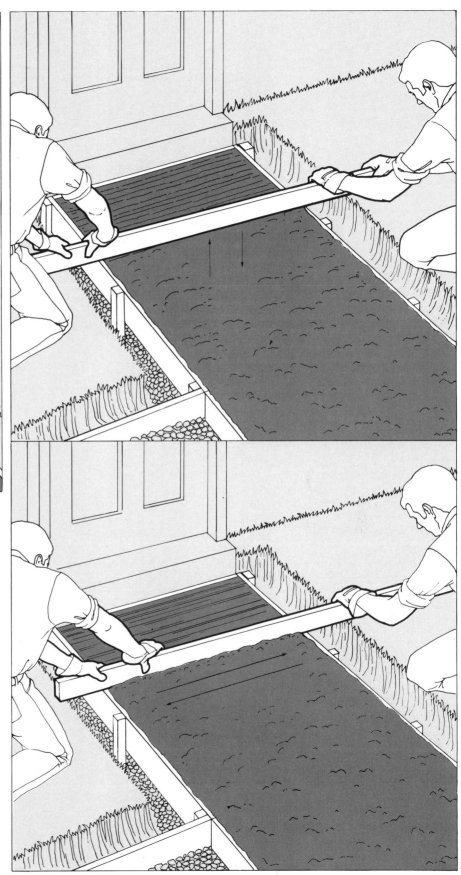

2 **Spading the edges.** As soon as one section is completely filled with concrete, drive a flat spade down between the concrete and the inner edges of the forms so as to force large aggregate away from the outside of the slab.

3 **Striking off the concrete.** Compact and level the slab with a tamping beam—a 50 mm thick length of timber placed on edge and cut about 500 mm wider than the forms—to strike off the concrete. Lift and push down *(right, above)* to compact the concrete. Then zigzag the board *(right)* to remove any excess concrete. If there is no excess, the concrete is probably under-compacted. Spread more concrete and re-tamp.

If you want a rippled, slip-proof finish, make a final pass with the tamping beam, moving it forwards by half its width with each up-and-down movement and at right angles to the form boards. Proceed directly to Step 2 overleaf.

To cover concrete with coloured mortar, make a tamping beam of two pieces, one to fit down 25 mm between the forms, the other to slide along the tops of form boards. When the surface looks dry, pour in mortar and strike off again—this time level with the tops of the forms. Then proceed as for uncoloured concrete.

If you plan to embed stones in the surface of the slab, complete the striking-off process and then turn to the instructions on page 55.

4 Floating the surface. Working quickly, smooth the concrete and eliminate any slight bumps or hollows with a darby—a board about 100 mm wide and 1 metre long with a handle attached. Pressing down lightly on the trailing edge of the darby, sweep it back and forth across the surface in wide arcs to force large aggregate down into the concrete. When water floats to the surface, stop darbying and wait until the water evaporates before finishing the surface or edging and jointing the slab.

If you plan to create a flagstone finish, complete the floating process and then turn to the instructions on pages 54 and 55.

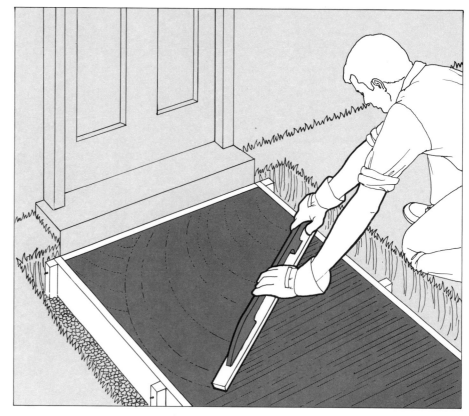

The Final Touches

1 Finishing the surface. As soon as bleed water has evaporated and the shiny surface turned dull, smooth and compact the concrete with a wood float. Keeping the float pressed flat, sweep it back and forth in gentle curves. Support yourself on a second float if you need to lean over the concrete. If the slab is too wide to reach across, make a bridge with a sturdy plank of wood supported outside the forms by several bricks or blocks. Move backwards as you work, smoothing out any marks you might have made by accidentally leaning or kneeling on the concrete.

2 **Rounding the side edges.** Draw a small trowel along the inner edges of the forms *(right)* to cut the top 20 to 25 mm of concrete away from the wood. Then finish the sides of the slab by running an edging tool *(far right)* firmly back and forth until the edges are round and smooth.

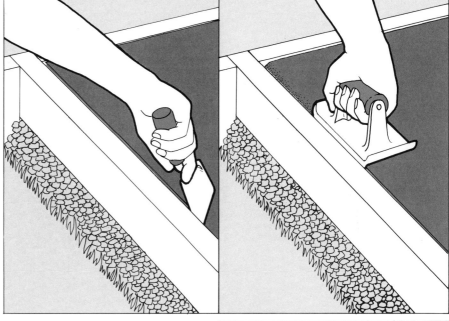

3 **Cutting control joints.** Make a 20 mm deep control joint across the slab every metre, to form roughly square sections between control joints. Place a length of T-iron, cut to the width of the slab, between the form boards; check with a square to make sure that it is perpendicular to the outside edges. Then press it into the concrete by tapping it with a mallet. Carefully remove the T-iron. If the slab is too wide to lean across, make a bridge of wood and bricks as described in Step 1.

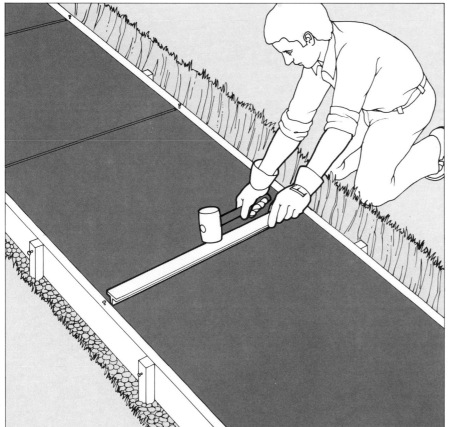

4 **Curing the slab.** Wet the concrete and keep it damp for three to four days in normal conditions or up to 10 days in very warm weather. Cover it tightly with polythene sheeting anchored with bricks; you can also use several layers of soaking-wet hessian sacks or old rugs, which must be kept damp by frequent sprinkling with a hose.

Special Finishes and Textures

A textured surface or design can add visual interest—and a safer foothold—to a concrete slab. The surfaces shown in these photographs are easily applied by using the techniques sketched.

Two of the finishes incorporate safety features into their design: embedding stones or making grooves in the surface will improve its tread. The simulated flagstone effect and the highly smooth surface, on the other hand, serve to provide decorative veneers for your path or patio.

Creating a smooth surface. To finish a slab with a silky surface, wait until bleed water has evaporated and work the surface with a wood float. Then work it again one, two or even three times with a steel float, depending on the degree of smoothness desired. For the first floating, keep the blade nearly flat against the concrete, and sweep the float back and forth in arcs ½ to 1 metre wide. Wait a few moments to let the concrete harden slightly between floatings. Use more pressure and a successively higher lift to the front edge of the blade *(below, left)* for each additional floating. With each floating, the recognizable float marks on the surface will become fainter and will have almost disappeared after the third time. Work until no concrete collects on the float and the tool makes a ringing sound as you sweep it across the slab.

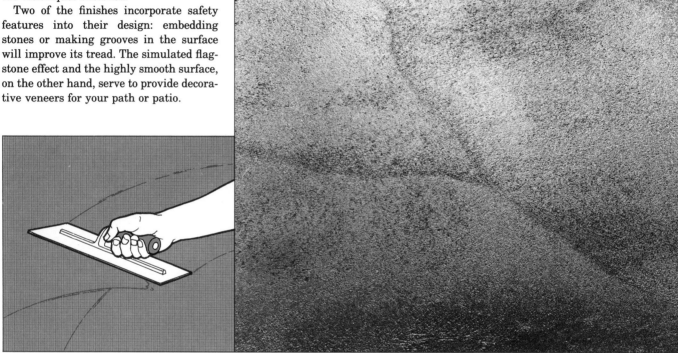

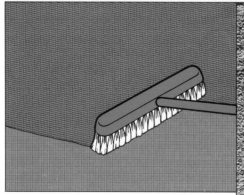

Brushing on a non-skid surface. To give concrete a rough, safe surface like that in the photograph on the right, draw a broom across the concrete after you finish working it with a wood float. A stiff-bristled broom will produce a coarser effect than a soft broom. Sweep straight lines at right angles to the sides or, if you want a curved pattern, move the broom in arcs. If the broom kicks up small lumps of concrete, hose the broom clean and let the slab dry for a few minutes before you proceed. If you have to press down heavily to score the surface with the broom, work fast; the concrete will soon be too hard to take this finish.

Embedding stones. Coloured stones inlaid in concrete create an attractive, skid-proof surface. Crushed stone, 20 to 40mm in diameter, is available from builders' merchants, who will deliver the proper amount for your slab. Wet the stones so they will not absorb water from the concrete and spread them over the slab after tamping. Stones can be dropped randomly to create a terrazzo effect *(below)* or placed in circles, squares or any design you wish. Tap the stones down with a large wood float or a darby *(below, right)* until the tops are just under the concrete surface. If you cannot force the stones down with the darby, use a brick. Then level with the darby. After bleed water disappears, place a board over the slab. When you can stand on the board without pushing the stones farther down, brush the concrete until each stone projects from the surface. Flush away excess concrete with fine spray from a hose-pipe *(below, centre)*. Do not expose more than the top third of the stones. Cover the concrete to begin curing; after a day or two, uncover it and wash the stones with water. Cure for two more days.

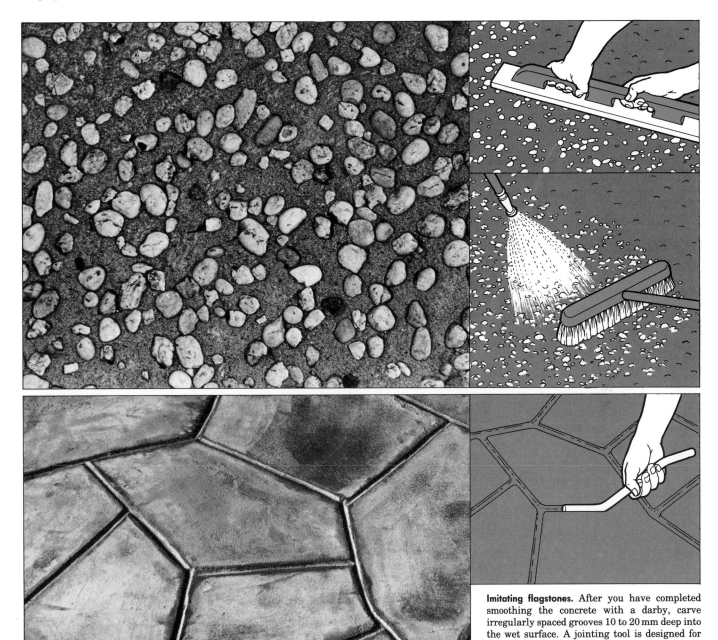

Imitating flagstones. After you have completed smoothing the concrete with a darby, carve irregularly spaced grooves 10 to 20 mm deep into the wet surface. A jointing tool is designed for this purpose, but you can also use a length of copper pipe bent into an S-shape *(above)*.

When the bleed water evaporates, trowel the concrete and retool the grooves until the flagstone-like pattern shows distinctly. Then brush the grooves carefully with a dry paint brush to clean out loose bits of concrete that remain.

What Goes Wrong and Why

When a concrete slab is correctly poured and finished it is nearly indestructible, but faults in preparation, working or finishing can lead to the defective surfaces shown in these photographs.

Overworking the surface with a float or darby is a primary cause of concrete failure. Such overworking sends aggregate towards the bottom of the slab and brings too much water and cement up. If the top of the slab contains too little aggregate, which provides strength, the surface will eventually break up.

Inadequate curing is a second problem. If a slab dries out or freezes and thaws too soon after pouring, severe surface damage will be the result.

The third common cause of defects is an incorrect mixture. Too much cement or water will weaken the entire slab. If you use aggregate containing soft stones or clay lumps instead of hard gravel, the surface may break down under normal wear and weather conditions.

Dusting. The grey powder on the finger on the left is picked up by a touch on a surface that has been overworked with a darby or float. Too much working weakens the top layer by dividing the concrete mixture—heavy aggregate sinks to the bottom, leaving too much water and cement on top. These light elements are not strong enough to withstand normal wear. Dusting may also occur if the slab has been cured for less than three to four days.

To stop dusting, brush the surface well to remove loose material. Then apply a concrete sealer, available at builders' merchants.

Spalling. Reinforcement, placed too near the surface, is bared by the flaking away of the thin layer of concrete over it. Such spalling also occurs in unreinforced slabs if the surface is weakened by too much floating.

You can repair a spalled concrete surface by patching it as illustrated on page 21. However, if the spalling is due to reinforcement being too near the surface, the repair will only have a temporary effect. If the spalling recurs, you will have to call in a professional.

Scaling. A concrete mixture containing too much water will lack strength throughout when it dries, and the weak top layer may crumble. Scaling may also occur if a slab subjected to freezing and thawing or to de-icing salts has not been made with air-entrained concrete.

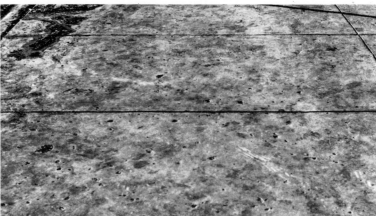

Popouts. If the aggregate contains lumps of clay or crumbly stones, these soft elements will deteriorate and wash away when the concrete has dried, leaving ugly holes in the surface called popouts. Make sure that the aggregate you use contains only hard gravel to avoid this defect.

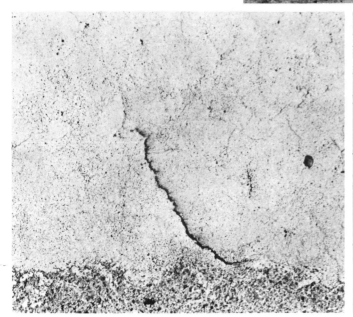

Cracking. Large cracks like these open up in concrete that contains too much water and cement, or that was poured so rapidly it could not be compacted properly. Spade freshly poured concrete thoroughly to force it into all corners of the form. Do not let a batch of concrete dry before pouring the next batch against it: cracks may appear at the boundary between the two pours.

Crazing. A network of hairline cracks may spoil the surface of a concrete mixture that contains too much cement; such an over-rich mixture shrinks more than a normal one when it dries, which leads to cracks. Lack of sufficient curing is another cause of cracking.

For a Large Slab: Reinforcement

All the techniques for building a small concrete slab, such as a path, are used in making a large one for a patio, drive or play area. There is one addition: a reinforcement of wire mesh. It is needed to help hold the concrete together against cracking under the heavy loads—often pressing in opposite directions—that a big slab may get, and also to resist the natural shrinkage of newly poured concrete, which is negligible in small sections but adds up in big ones.

Specific requirements for reinforcing concrete may be included in your local building regulations. Therefore, before you start one of these large projects, be sure to check with your local authorities.

Wire-mesh reinforcement, which looks like heavy fencing, comes in standard rolls or sheets, sold in various weights. For a patio or a drive, the mesh size should be 200 by 200 mm, meaning the wires are 200 mm apart in each direction. The wire should be between 3 and 5 mm in diameter.

Builder's merchants sometimes charge a high fee for cutting mesh to size, and you may save by buying a whole roll and cutting it yourself, even if some is left over, or by buying several sheets.

Cut reinforcement 50 mm smaller than the forms, building up sections wider than the maximum width of the roll or sheet by overlapping pieces by 150 mm and binding

them together with thinner wire. If the reinforcement was bought in rolls, walk over the mesh to flatten out the waves, formed while it was in roll form, once you have completed preparations for pouring. Wear gloves to protect your hands.

With several workers to help with the finishing steps, you can pour a fairly large patio in one day, using ready-mix concrete from a lorry. But if you prefer to mix your own concrete and pour it in small batches, you can either fill the sections one at a time, removing the temporary form boards at the expansion joints as each section hardens, or you can construct a patio with permanent forms *(page 61)*.

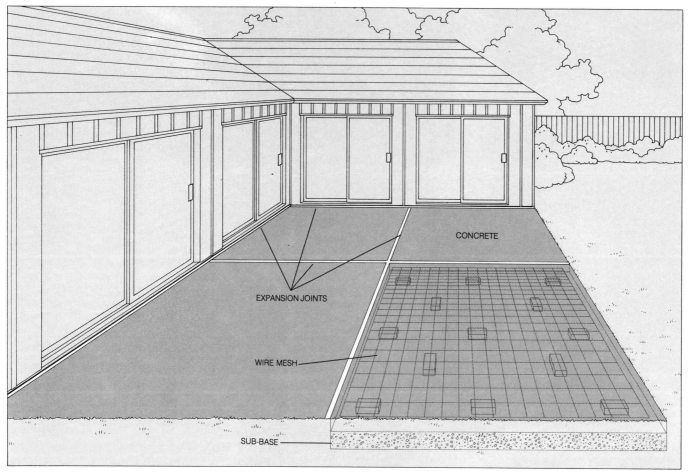

Anatomy of a reinforced slab. A 100 mm sub-base of hoggin or crushed stone—if required—is topped by wire-mesh reinforcement to strengthen the 100 mm of concrete for a large slab such as this patio. Expansion joints are placed 5 to 6 metres apart in both directions in the slab, and between the slab and an abutting structure such as the house. Control joints are not necessary in a reinforced slab. A patio is sloped in one direction only, away from the house, so that water will run off it. How a drive is sloped depends on the contours of land near the garage.

Making a Patio

1 **Sloping a patio.** Lay out the patio, excavate the site and place support stakes, following the instructions for a path *(pages 42–45)*. However, plan to place stakes inside form boards, and leave an extra 10 mm of space between the house and the stakes to accommodate the expansion joints. To slope the patio so that its gradient will carry water away from the house, mark the stakes along the edge of the house at the desired level. Then at each stake 2 metres away, pencil a line 25 mm below the levelling marks. Another 2 metres away, drop the slope to 50 mm below the marks, and so on. Attach form boards *(pages 47–48)*, using the marks as guides for board tops.

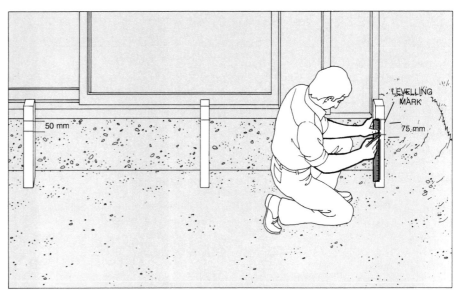

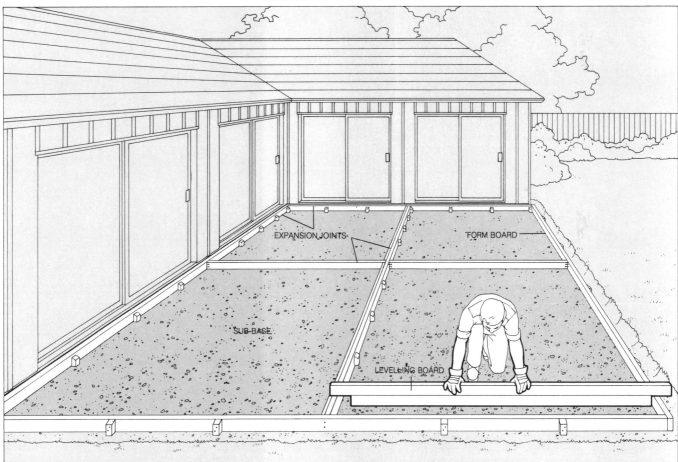

2 **Expansion joints and sub-base.** Place expansion joint filler against the house and build forms next to it, using 1 metre lengths of fairly small timber, 50 by 100 mm in size, which are easier to pull out after the concrete has been poured. Divide the patio into sections no larger than 6 by 6 metres. Set up additional form boards running the length of the patio, with stakes on the side away from the section that will be poured first. Lay a sub-base 100 mm deep, if one is required, and level one section at a time. Across the width of the patio, place expansion joint filler, holding it in place with four 90 mm nails driven part of the way into the form boards *(page 49)*.

3 **Laying the wire mesh.** Place the cut end of rolled wire mesh 50 mm from the form board and weight it with a brick or block. Walk backwards, unrolling the wire mesh. Cut it off 50 mm from the form board at the other end of the patio section. Because the wire is stiff, the ends will remain curled. With a helper, turn the mesh over and flatten it by walking on it. Bind the ends of the wire together where two strips overlap. If the mesh was bought in sheets, simply cut them so that they are 50 mm smaller than the section, and lay the mesh in place. Just before pouring the concrete, pick up the wire mesh and support it 50 mm above the base with bricks, stones or plastic spacers set 600 mm to 1 metre apart.

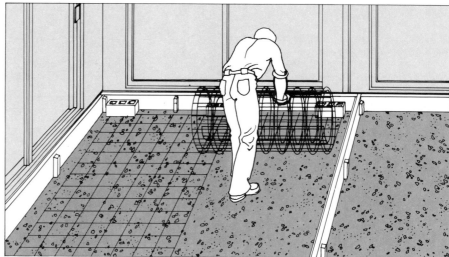

4 **Removing form boards and filling spaces.** After striking off the poured concrete *(page 51)* in each section, build a bridge with a ladder supported by bricks or blocks and topped with a plank. One at a time, pry up sections of the perimeter form board with a crowbar. Lift them out by pulling upwards and wiggling them from side to side to loosen the stakes. Leave the centre boards temporarily in place. Shovel concrete into the resulting spaces *(right)* and finish it off with a darby. After pouring the adjacent section, extend the ladder to span both sections. Pull the form boards from the centre after striking off the adjacent sections.

5 **Skip floating.** When you cannot reach to the middle of a large slab, use a tool called a skip float in place of a darby for finishing. You can make a skip float easily. Use a board about 25 mm thick, 200 mm wide and between 1 and 1½ metres long. Bevel the long edges and sand them smooth. Cut two small blocks of wood slightly narrower than the width of the base, and drill holes through them to form an attachment for the handle. Screw the blocks on to the base so that they are parallel to each other. The space between them should be slightly larger than the diameter of the handle you will be using. For the handle, drill a hole near one end of a 3 to 5 metre length of wood or rigid plastic water pipe. Attach it to the base by placing it between the blocks and then passing a bolt through the pre-drilled holes in the handle and the blocks. The bolt will form a hinge which will allow the handle to swivel. Work the skip float back and forth, letting it skim the surface of the concrete. If the concrete begins to stiffen, weight the skip float with a couple of bricks.

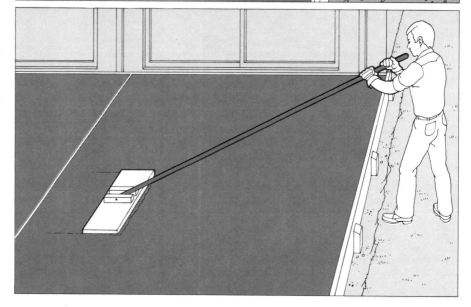

A Patio Poured in Sections

Making permanent forms. Forms made from wood that has been professionally treated with a preservative can stay in place permanently, permitting you to divide a large patio into a grid of small sections to be poured a few at a time. Any rectangular pattern that pleases you will serve, but keep the sections no larger than 3 square metres, the amount someone can finish before the concrete begins to harden. Avoid patterns that include L or T-shaped sections.

Bricks that are placed on edge can be substituted for permanent wooden forms. Bed the bricks firmly in the ground and, if necessary, adjust the depth of the sub-base or the concrete to make sure that the finished surface of the slab will be flush with the top of the bricks.

Building Permanent Forms

1 Laying out the grid. Place the support stakes for perimeter forms inside the form boards. Except at the corners, drive them 25 mm below the boards so that the stakes will not show. After completing the perimeter forms, lay out the grid pattern with strings and stakes, maintaining the slope of the patio from house to outside edge. At each point where strings cross, drive a 200 mm long, preservative-treated stake into the base. Then establish the line for the bottom of the form boards by running a length of taut string from underneath the perimeter form boards to intersect the stakes. Using a sledge hammer, drive the stakes down to that level.

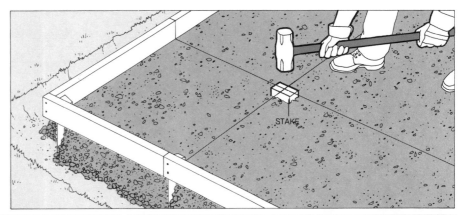

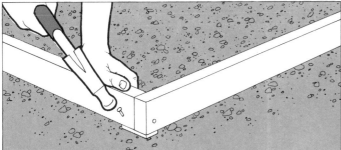

2 Securing the forms to stakes. Rest one form board on a stake and drive a 75 mm galvanized nail into it at an angle to fasten it to the stake. Butt another board against the first and secure it with an angled nail. Then nail through the first board into the end of the second.

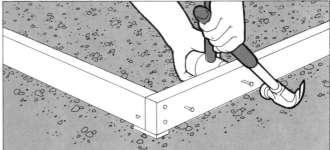

3 Nailing the sides of the forms. To bind the concrete to the form boards, drive 75 mm galvanized nails into the sides of the boards about half way between top and bottom and at 300 mm intervals. Hold a mallet or hammer on the opposite side of the board to prevent it from moving, and leave about half the nail sticking out. Protect the tops of the boards with heavy-duty masking tape while pouring and finishing the concrete.

Working Round Obstacles

The techniques for laying a slab of concrete shown on pages 42–53 are fine for most concreting jobs. Occasionally, however, you may face special obstacles—when the slab abuts a wall that limits your working space, for example, or when an irremovable object such as a manhole or inspection cover protrudes from the surface you plan to cover. The problems posed by such inconveniences are easily solved by adaptations of already familiar techniques.

If you intend to lay a slab alongside a wall, you will not have room to use a tamping beam to strike off the concrete, as shown on page 51. Instead you will have to create working surfaces for your helper and yourself by dividing the slab into bays that are concreted alternately. After pouring and finishing the concrete for one set of bays, you will be able to stand on the hardened concrete in order to install concrete in the intervening spaces.

The alternate bay method is also useful when constructing a path or drive down a steep slope. By dividing the slab into bays, you can insert across the width of the drive temporary form boards that will minimize the tendency of fresh concrete to slump downhill. Once the poured sections have hardened, the boards can be removed and the empty bays filled and finished.

If concrete is poured directly round a rigid inspection cover for a manhole or a gully grating, it may crack. You can avoid this danger by placing temporary form boards round the obstacle to make an expansion joint. If the inspection cover falls in the middle of a slab, you will save time and effort by aligning one of the existing expansion joints with one side of the cover.

Concreting in Alternate Bays

Laying a path alongside a wall. Place expansion joint filler along the length of the wall; build the form work as shown on pages 42–48. Remember to keep the top of the form work—and the surface of the finished slab—at least 150 mm below the damp-proof course in the wall. Set form boards perpendicular to the wall across the sub-base at intervals of not more than 3 metres.

Stake the form boards on alternate sides. Pour and finish concrete in alternate bays, standing in the empty bays to tamp the fresh concrete *(below)*. Cure the concrete for one to two days until it is hard enough to stand on without being marked. Remove the form boards and pour and finish concrete in the empty bays, standing on the hard concrete when using the tamping beam.

Boxing in a Rigid Obstacle

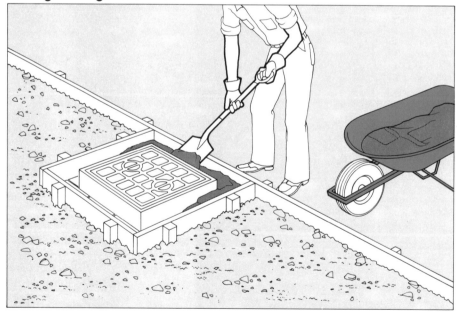

Isolating an inspection cover. Before pouring the slab, construct an expansion joint all the way round the inspection cover by building a box of temporary form boards. The box should be large enough to include any masonry surrounding the cover. Stake the form boards on the outside of the box. If possible, use the edge of the slab or an expansion joint within the slab for one side of the box. Shovel the concrete inside the box round the cover *(above)*. Leave the concrete to cure for one to two days before removing the form boards. Place expansion joint filler round the concrete and then pour and finish the rest of the slab.

Extending an Existing Slab

Sometimes a new concrete slab must be connected to an existing structure. You may want to enlarge a patio, for example, or carry a path round the house, or add a turning area to the drive. There are two possible ways to handle such extensions, depending on the soil in which the planned addition will be laid. If it is firm and sandy, then the addition should be constructed just as a section of new slab would be (pages 49 and 59). The new concrete should be poured up to the edge of the existing slab—shrinkage in the fresh concrete will provide the necessary expansion joint between the two slabs.

However, if the addition is to be laid on clayey or peaty soil, or if the ground has to be made up to the level of the existing slab, then the two slabs should be bound together with 500 mm lengths of steel reinforcing rod at least 10 mm in diameter. (The rod, available from builders' merchants, can be cut to length with a hacksaw.) If the two sections are not bound together as described below, settlement in the new slab may cause the joint between the two slabs to become "stepped".

Locking Together Old and New Concrete

1 **Installing reinforcing rod.** Excavate the area of the extension and remove any dirt or damaged concrete from the edge of the old slab. Using a hammer-action power drill with a carbide-tipped masonry bit 2 mm larger than the reinforcing rod, drill holes 50 to 75 mm deep into the edge of the old slab. Position the first hole 150 mm in from the edge and space the others 300 mm apart. Clear the holes by squirting water into them from a hose. Fix reinforcing rod into the holes with epoxy resin, keeping the rods parallel with the base of the new slab. If the extension is more than 2 metres wide, coat the exposed ends of the bars with heavy grease. The grease will allow the bars to move horizontally and prevent cracking when the new concrete shrinks.

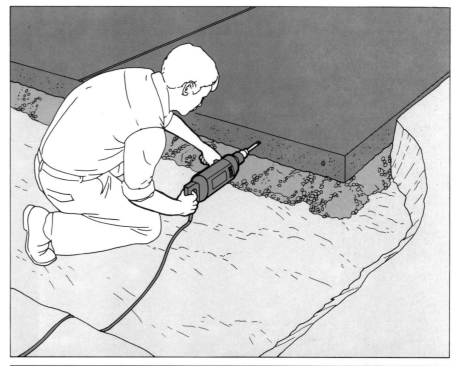

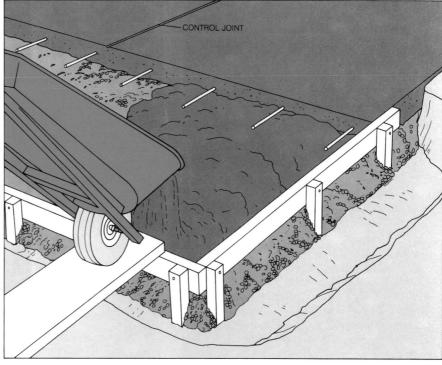

CONTROL JOINT

2 **Pouring the addition.** Construct forms as on page 42 and add a 100 mm sub-base of crushed stone or hoggin, if required. If the addition straddles a section of patio or drive already intersected by an expansion joint, install a matching expansion joint in the forms for the extension, as described on page 49. Thoroughly wet the edges of the old slab; then pour the concrete. Finish the new slab as on pages 51–53, scoring it with control joints, as needed, to match the control joints in the old slab. Leave the forms in place for a week.

Sturdy Footings for Strong Walls

Below the base of a wall or a building, usually concealed by earth or turf, lies a vital structural element—the footing. It is supported by solid ground and in turn it supports all the weight of the structure above, which may be a 1 metre high garden wall or a three storey high house. Whatever its load, the footing almost always takes the form of a long, narrow, flat-topped strip.

Footings designed for the light, low brick and stone walls described in this book do not differ much from an ordinary concrete slab, poured just below the surface of the ground. Such strip footings do not need wooden forms: a straight-sided trench will serve for pouring concrete. For right-angle turns, the footing corners must be true right angles. Follow the 3-4-5 triangle on the opposite page to set them out.

The footings for high, free-standing walls are more complex and almost always governed by building regulations. The techniques involved in constructing such strong, load-bearing footings are best attempted only after the fundamentals of building simpler footings, like the one shown on the right, have been mastered.

The first step in constructing a strip footing is to work out the dimensions of the trench into which the concrete will be poured. The trench should be twice the width of the finished wall, and should extend by half this distance—the width of a single brick—beyond each end of the wall. The bottom of the trench must be at least 350 mm below ground level, even in firm ground; if you are building on clayey soil, dig down as far as necessary until you reach firm soil. The concrete in the footing should be at least 250 mm thick—in a 350 mm deep trench, this means that the top of the concrete will be about 100 mm below the ground, and the first 1½ courses of bricks will be covered by soil when the wall is completed. You will then be able to place soil for planting against the wall.

A footing can be made with a relatively weak mix because concrete beneath the ground is not subject to wear or weathering. Follow the recipe for foundation mix on page 26. To calculate the number of cubic metres of concrete needed, multiply the length of the trench by its width by the thickness of the concrete, in metres.

A Footing for a Low, Straight Wall

1 **Excavating the trench.** A garden wall less than 1.2 metres high can rest on a footing made like a long, narrow slab that floats above the frost line; as a general rule, such a footing needs no reinforcing. Dig a trench of the required dimensions, keeping the sides and bottom as straight as possible. Do not follow the natural slope of the land. To set the level, drive a stake into the bottom of the trench; its top marks the height of the concrete. Drive in another stake a metre away and check that the tops are level with a straight length of wood and a level. Drive in more stakes along the trench, checking the level each time (below). On steeply sloping ground, step the trench every ½ to 1 metre. The dimensions of each step should be multiples of the brick size.

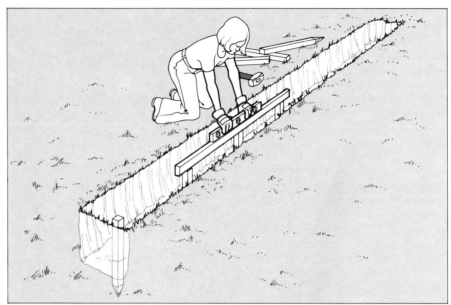

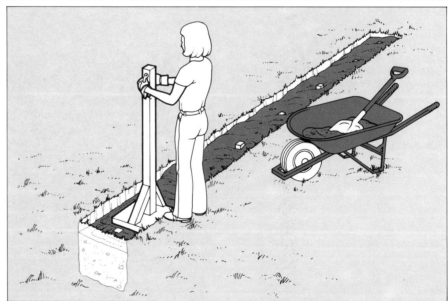

2 **Pouring the concrete.** Mix and pour concrete for the footing as you would for an ordinary slab (pages 50–53). Compact the concrete thoroughly with a tamper made by nailing and bracing a sturdy piece of wood about half a metre long to a square board. Nail two door handles to the top, one positioned on each side. Level the surface of the concrete so that it is flush with the tops of the stakes, taking care not to dislodge them, and then leave the concrete to cure.

Right-Angle Corners

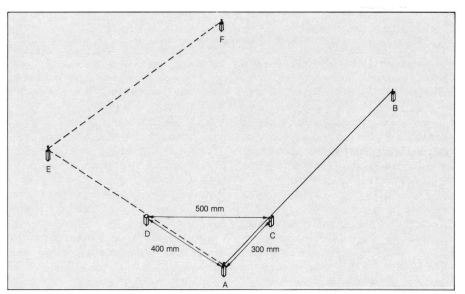

1 **Setting out.** To make a right-angle corner for a wall, use the 3-4-5 triangle method to line up footings. Stake one building line (AB) in relation to a property boundary or an existing structure. Along this line, exactly 300 mm from stake A, set stake C and drive a nail in it at the 300 mm mark directly under the AB line. Tie a 500 mm long string to the nail in stake C and a 400 mm string to the nail in stake A. Where the ends of the strings meet, set stake D. These three stakes should form a triangle with sides of 300, 400 and 500 mm. Check the lengths with a steel tape (strings may stretch) and adjust stake D as needed. Extend the line from A through D to E, completing a second building line. For a third line, repeat the 3-4-5 triangle process at point E.

2 **Setting up profile boards.** At least a metre outside the corner stakes, erect four profile boards. Each consists of two lengths of wood nailed to three stakes, and set in a right angle that encloses a corner stake. Transfer the strings of the building plan from the corner stakes to the profile boards, using a plumb line to make sure the strings intersect precisely over the corner stakes. Mark string ends on the boards with a nail.

Remove strings and corner stakes so you can dig a footing trench—the plan can always be reconstructed by running strings from the marked points on the profile boards. Mark the profile boards to fix lines outside the building plan to locate the outer edge of the footing. The distance from this line to the building line should equal half the width of the completed wall. You can mark these lines directly on the ground by running strings between the profile boards and dribbling sand over the strings. The lines will show as straight, unsanded lengths along the ground.

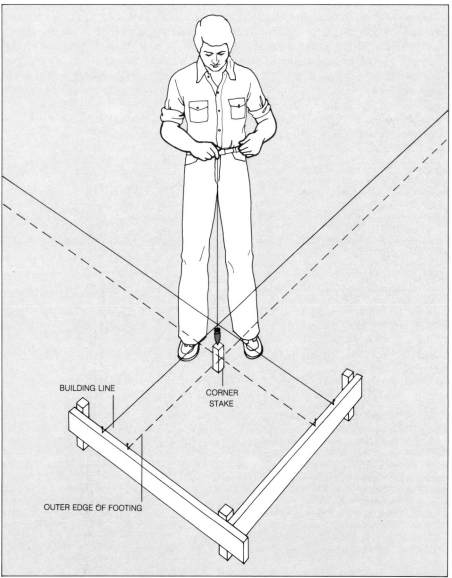

Rugged Steps of Poured Concrete

When you need to replace worn-out wooden stairs outdoors, or provide new ones for an added doorway, poured concrete is often the best choice: concrete steps are fairly simple to make and, once built, are all but indestructible. The method shown here, based on standard form-building and pouring techniques, is suitable for a structure no more than about 750 mm high.

The only tricky part of building four or fewer steps is laying out the steps' profile on the plywood form sides: the design should not be a series of rectangular jogs but, for comfort and weather resistance, a very gentle saw-tooth, with the tops, or treads, sloping down and the vertical sections, or risers, sloping forwards *(right, below)*. For safety, it is crucial to get the dimensions right. The depth of the tread must be related to the height of the riser, and these two dimensions should total about 450 mm. Theoretically, an extremely high riser can be used with a shallow tread, or vice versa, provided their sum meets the standard. As a practical matter, however, risers should be 150 to 200 mm high, and they should be combined with treads of 300 to 250 mm. You will have to determine the dimensions for your project by measuring and calculating *(Step 2)*.

With the dimensions settled, you can draw plans and estimate materials. After you have worked out the required amount of concrete *(page 40)*, you can mix what you need in a power mixer, using the general purpose recipe given on page 26, but it is usually simpler to order from a ready-mix company. You will also need five-ply plywood; timber for forms and braces; double-headed nails; crushed stone or hoggin for a sub-base, if one is required; release agent—available from builders' merchants—which is spread on the forms to prevent them from sticking to the concrete; and bituminized felt and exterior-grade flexible sealant to make a joint, sealing the space between the steps and house. The sub-base is simple to make alone, but when the ready-mix lorry arrives, get a friend to help you move the concrete from the lorry to the plywood form in a wheelbarrow, and shovel it into place.

1 Finding the height. Level the ground approximately 2 metres in front of the door. Then measure from the ground to the underside of the sill. This will be the rise—the vertical distance that the finished stairs will fill.

2 Calculating dimensions. All steps should be at least 150 mm wider than the door opening. The top-most step, or landing, should be at least 1 metre deep to provide an area for entering and leaving safely. Divide the rise found in Step 1 by the number of steps you wish to build to find the height of each riser. Subtract the riser height from 450 mm to find the tread width. Thus, if the rise comes to 600 mm, you could make three steps, each with a 200 mm riser and a 250 mm tread or, alternatively, four gentle steps, each with a 150 mm riser and 300 mm tread. From the dimensions you arrive at, make a plan and estimate the materials required.

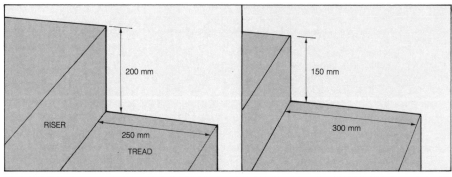

3 Cutting side forms. Lay out the sides of the forms on a sheet of five-ply plywood using the dimensions selected in Step 2. Make the height of the forms 300 mm greater than the rise, since 300 mm of concrete and sub-base will be below ground level. On firm soils which do not require a sub-base, make the height of the forms only 200 mm greater than the rise. First draw risers and treads at right angles, using a steel square. Slope each tread and the platform downwards (dotted lines) to provide drainage, pitching them 6 mm for each 300 mm of depth. Slope the risers 15 degrees forwards (dotted lines).

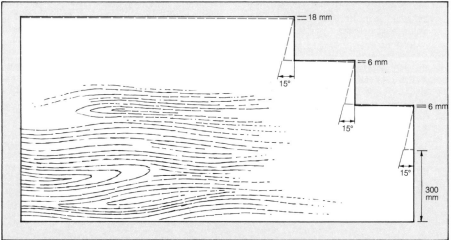

4 **Setting up the form sides.** Dig a hole 300 mm deep—200 mm if you are not laying a sub-base—and about 25 mm larger all round than the steps. Tamp the ground firmly at the bottom of the hole. Nail vertical braces to the outsides of the form sides. Place the form sides against the sides of the hole, 10 mm away from the house wall, using a steel square to make sure they are at right angles to the house, and a level to check that the edges are truly horizontal and vertical. Drive stakes at least 200 mm into the ground about 450 mm away from the hole. Nail braces between the form sides and the stakes. Pour in 100 mm of crushed stone or hoggin for the sub-base and tamp it level.

5 **Completing the form.** Cut pieces of timber to fit the risers, bevelling the bottom edges so that your trowel will be able to reach and smooth the entire surface of the tread after the concrete is poured. Nail the riser boards to the form sides with double-headed nails. When the form is completely in place, set bituminized felt against the house foundation, and seal it with exterior-grade flexible sealant *(right)* for an expansion joint. Coat inside surfaces of the forms with release agent to prevent the concrete from sticking to them as it cures.

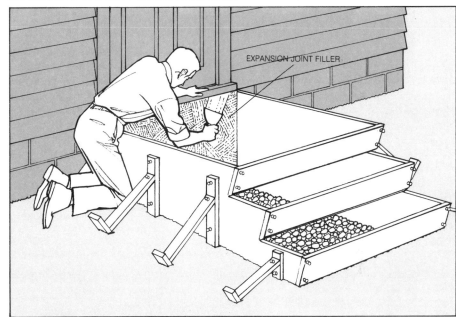

EXPANSION JOINT FILLER

6 **Pouring concrete into the form.** If the mixer or delivery lorry can be brought close to the job, pour concrete directly into the form through a trough; otherwise you will have to use a wheelbarrow. Begin by pouring concrete into the lowest step; when it is full, pour or shovel concrete into the second step. If the riser boards bulge outwards, brace them with additional stakes *(inset)*.

Pour enough concrete to overfill the form slightly. Drive shovels into every corner to make sure the form is completely filled and air pockets are eliminated. When pouring is completed, plunge shovels down into the concrete along the inside edges of the form to force large aggregate away from the outside edge of the concrete.

Blend and smooth the freshly poured concrete as shown on pages 50–53, finishing the surfaces after the bleed water has evaporated, and then cure the structure for a week. Finally, when the steps are cured, you can remove the forms.

Creating Free-Form Shapes: a Bowl for a Pool

Pouring concrete in the shape of a bowl is even simpler than pouring it for a slab, and the technique involved makes a variety of useful, decorative structures. A water-filled bowl, sunk flush to the surface of a lawn or garden, serves as a paddling pool or a picturesque setting for statuary. A recirculating pump turns the bowl into a fountain. With a run-off channel in the rim of the bowl, it becomes a fish pond (below). Any of these structures can be built without wooden forms. Generally, the concrete can be poured directly on to tamped earth without a sub-base. Since a bowl bears little weight, its concrete sides and base need be no thicker than 100 mm.

Small concrete bowls for any purpose can be constructed like the fish pond shown on these pages, which is 2 metres long, 1 to 2 metres wide and 600 mm deep. It requires just under half a cubic metre of concrete, is small enough to fit into a small garden and is so shallow that its 1,600 litres of water are self-aerating. You can probably mix and finish the concrete by yourself in a single day, although an assistant will make the work easier. Follow the recipe for the paving mix given on page 26. To order ready-mix concrete, refer to the instructions for ordering air-entrained concrete on page 41.

In other phases of construction you will use some tools and techniques that differ from those designed for slabs. An ordinary square or rectangular tamper, for instance, is too angular for the bowl's rounded con-tours—but a spare tyre turns out to be perfect for tamping. A length of plastic round the top of a shaped excavation keeps dirt from mixing with the concrete. The same wire reinforcing mesh used in a slab is also used in the bowl, but it must be bent into the proper shape first. And a bowl, like a slab, must be covered during the curing process with further plastic sheeting.

If the finished bowl is to contain water, it must be sealed. For a paddling pool, any waterproof paint or silicone sealer will do. If you intend to use the bowl as a fish pond, buy a neutralizing agent in powder form from an aquarium supplier or a garden centre. When the powder is mixed with water, it becomes a paint that both seals the pond and neutralizes the alkalis in the freshly cured concrete. When the concrete has cured for three days, fill the pond with water; leave it for a week and then change all the water. Repeat this procedure twice before introducing fish into the pond.

Stock a fish pond or water-plant pool carefully with species suited to your pond and climate—a specialist pond and aquarium supplier will give you professional advice. Some of the more commonly recommended species of fish are goldfish, fantails, shubunkins and golden orfe. Snails and tadpoles will probably colonize your pond naturally in time, but both can also be purchased. Use weighted pots or boxes, known as planting crates, on the pond floor for oxygenating plants like Canadian pondweed, elodea crispa and hawnwort, and for purely decorative water lilies. Water hyacinths and duckweed will float, roots and all, on the surface.

The Anatomy of a Concrete Bowl

75 mm

100 mm CONCRETE

WIRE MESH

600 mm   700 mm

60°

RUN-OFF CHANNEL

A pond made without forms. The excavation for a bowl like this fish pond must be 100 mm larger in every dimension than the inner concrete wall and floor of the finished bowl. Because the concrete is poured without forms, the sides of the hole must slope at an angle of no more than 60 or 70 degrees—a steeper slope would cause the concrete, while it is being poured, to slide from the sides of the bowl to the bottom. Wire mesh (inset) reinforces the concrete. For a fish pond, a run-off channel cut into the rim permits excess water to flow away at a single point.

Preparing the Excavation

1 **Tamping the earth.** Outline the bowl with rope or a length of garden hose—for the fish pond shown in this demonstration, the outline should be roughly 2 by 1.2 metres with an extra allowance of 100 mm on all sides for the concrete—and mark the outline on the ground with a spade. Dig the excavation from the edges down until you reach a uniform bottom depth—for this fish pond, about 700 mm. Tamp and compact the earth by bouncing a spare tyre around the bottom and along the sides of the excavation.

2 **Laying in the reinforcing mesh.** Bend a single piece of 200 by 200 mm wire reinforcing mesh to fit inside the entire bowl shape of the excavation, cutting into the edges of the mesh to help mould it into the bowl shape. The fit does not have to be exact—the wire mesh need not reach all the way to the top. After shaping the mesh, remove it and run a continuous strip of heavy plastic sheeting round the top of the excavation, with the inner edge extending 300 mm down the sloped sides. Line the bottom and sides of the hole with 50 mm high stones or pieces of brick at 300 mm intervals; replace the mesh on these supports.

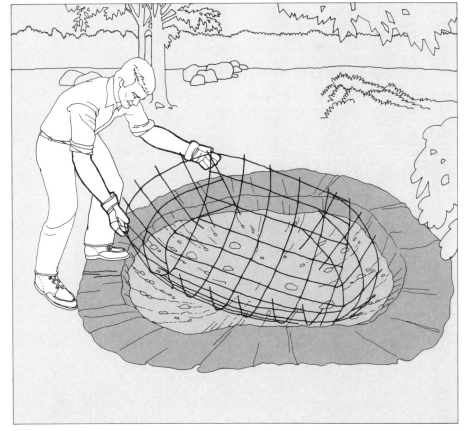

3 **Marking the thickness of the concrete.** The concrete lining of the bowl should be about 100 mm thick. To control the thickness, drive 250 mm long stakes cut from 50 by 50 mm timber at 300 mm intervals into the bottom and sides between the openings in the wire mesh. Mark a line 100 mm from the ground on each stake.

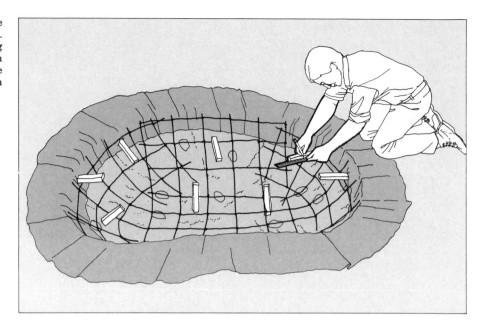

Shaping the Bowl

1 **Pouring and smoothing the concrete.** Pour the concrete into the centre of the excavation, then lay a sturdy wooden board across opposite sides of the hole, propping the ends up on bricks or blocks. Using the board as necessary for easy access to every part of the excavation, work the concrete outwards and up the sides with the back of a square shovel. If the mesh sinks below the 50 mm level of brick or stone supports at any point, lift the mesh with a rake. As you bring the concrete level up to the 100 mm marks on the stakes, pull the stakes out and fill the holes they leave with concrete. Shovel all excess concrete on to the plastic strip round the rim of the excavation. Finally, smooth the concrete with a wood float. To gain access to the steeply curving parts of the bowl, use a large rubber or plastic beach ball in place of the wood float.

2 Forming the lip. The simplest tool for edging the concrete round a small bowl is an ordinary large coffee can, or a cylindrical plastic container, with the ends removed and the body cut in half lengthwise. Using this as a portable mould, shape the concrete over the plastic rim, smoothing irregularities with a pointed trowel.

3 Making a run-off channel. After forming the lip, cut out a 75 mm wide semicircular section and embed into the opening 10 by 10 mm wire screening, bent double to avoid sharp points. The channel makes an overflow outlet in a downpour, while the wire screen will prevent fish from escaping.

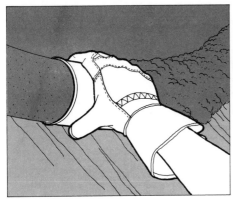

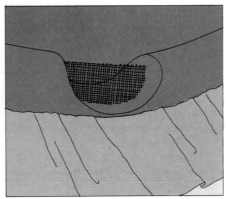

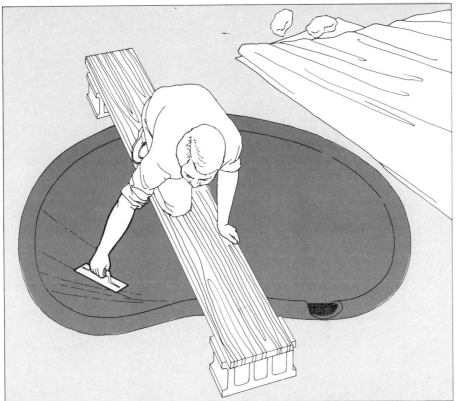

4 Floating and curing. Cut off the black plastic strip flush to the outside of the lip with scissors, and cover the entire pond, board and all, with plastic sheeting, weighted at the edges with bricks or stones. The covering will keep hairline cracks from developing in the concrete between three separate floatings. Wait 30 minutes to an hour, until all water sheen on the surface disappears, then go over the surface of the concrete with a small steel float. Cover the pond loosely again and wait about 45 minutes—at this point the concrete should be barely spongy to the touch and the weight of your hand should leave a faint impression—and float a second time. Cover the pond again for 45 minutes. On the third floating your hand should leave no impression in the concrete and the float should make a ringing noise as you work. Wait 10 to 15 minutes for any residual water to evaporate, then remove the work board. Lay the plastic sheeting directly on the concrete inside the bowl and up over the lip. Weight the edges with bricks or stones and spread a layer of sand over the sheeting to hold it down. Keep the concrete covered for three days while it cures.

How to Empty a Pond with a Siphon

Even in a moderately cool climate, a 600 mm deep fish pond can safely be left full throughout the year. If ice forms on the surface during the winter, it normally acts as an insulating skin that keeps the water below from freezing. However, in extremely cold climates or during a severe cold spell in moderate climates, make sure the ice is not freezing solid. Fish can live in a dormant state under a surface layer of ice, but they cannot survive a solid freeze; you will have to take them inside, along with your plants, for the duration of the winter or cold spell.

Regardless of the weather, you may want to drain the pond periodically for painting or cleaning. There are several ways to do the job, from bailing the water out with a bucket to pumping it out with a submersible power pump. But if your property has ground lower than the pond, you can siphon the water out with a garden hose-pipe.

The most efficient way to siphon with a hose is to attach it to a tap and run water through to force the air out. Then close the nozzle end tight and set it on the ground below the pond. Turn the tap on again and fill the hose completely. Finally, turn the tap off and unscrew the hose, cupping your hand over the end to hold the water in. Submerge the tap end of the hose in the pond and open the nozzle end; the water should immediately start to drain from the pond.

If your garden tap is inconveniently far from the pond, use this alternative, somewhat slower method: submerge the hose in the water with both ends open. When the hose is full (be patient—it will fill slowly, and it must be entirely full, with no air bubbles), cap one end with your hand and carry it to lower ground. Uncap the hose to let the water drain from the pond.

3

A Cornucopia of Blocks

For many, the pleasures of building with blocks reach a peak in the kindergarten years and fade away soon afterwards. For a lucky few, however, these delights last a lifetime, growing deeper and more complex with experience and skill. Such individuals find a compelling attraction in working with bricks, stones, tiles and concrete blocks. The planning of block paving or walls, the agreeably repetitive yet constantly changing task of fitting and mortaring the individual pieces, the sense of achievement at the completion of the job—these are the rewards of masonry as a hobby, and they increase for the individual with each passing year.

Curiously, the appeal of the builder's art has been especially notable among men known for their literary talents (as well as other things). Within the present century, critic H. L. Mencken and poet T. S. Eliot have both been enthusiastic amateur bricklayers. But the most famous of these part-time builders was Sir Winston Churchill. At Chartwell, his country estate, Churchill gave much of his spare time to projects that ranged from the laying of brick paths and garden walls to the building of small cottages. Whatever the brickwork task, he found satisfaction in it, for it brought rest and strength to what he called "the tired places" of his mind.

Such amateurs pursue their hobby for both aesthetic and practical ends. On the aesthetic side, there is the contrast of individual blocks on the one hand, and blocks massed in patterns on the other. With masonry blocks, the total effect becomes greater than the sum of the parts. Brick, concrete block, stone and tile create the kind of eye-catching patterns, made more dramatic by sunlight and shadow, that a monolithic material such as smooth, poured concrete ordinarily cannot be expected to produce.

Each category of block brings a special character to garden projects. Bricks give ruggedness and pleasing symmetry; concrete blocks give an impression of strength and massiveness, even though many of them are shaped like fretwork (*opposite page*) to form decorative screens; stones give an artless-seeming rusticity; tiles can give elegance and smoothness; and, in addition, there is enough variety in the choice of colours to inspire complex designs.

From a practical standpoint, blocks are easy to use. Unlike concrete, which presents a mass of material that sometimes must be dealt with in minutes and may also require a platoon of assistants, blocks can be installed over a period of several weeks and their assembly can be a project for one person. Even the children can participate in a job that uses bricks and tiles. The builder is able to set his own tempo, proceed just as far as he wants and stop when he decides to.

Modern Bricks: 10,000 Shapes, Sizes, Textures

Bricks have been used for at least 5,000 years and they are still the most popular building material for all sorts of structures, from walls, steps and fireplaces to paths and patios. Bricks are compact and light to handle yet also strong and durable. Their beauty seems to improve with age—a quality that has inspired some manufacturers to produce new ones that simulate the chipped edges, paint splatters and patina of old ones.

Modern bricks are made in more than 10,000 combinations of shape, size, colour and texture, but within this staggering array you will find that most bricks fit into three main categories: common, facing and paving bricks.

Common bricks are economically priced but often have a rough and unattractive finish. Most common bricks are not highly weather resistant and are typically used for internal house walls and for external brickwork that will be covered by rendering or facing masonry. Some types can be used for building garden walls: check with your supplier when purchasing. Facing bricks—which come in colours from almost white to purplish black, as well as in textures from rough to silky-smooth (opposite)—are resistant to water and frost and are suitable for almost all exposed brickwork. Both common and facing bricks are usually 215 mm long by 102.5 mm wide and 65 mm high, although many special shapes and sizes are also available. In Australia, common and facing bricks come in two main sizes: metric traditional bricks are 230 by 110 by 76 mm, and metric modular bricks are 290 by 90 by 90 mm.

Facing bricks are often too porous and soft to be laid for paths and patios. There you will want to use paving bricks, which are dense and often rough-surfaced. Some paving bricks are shallow—sometimes as little as 35 mm high—so that they can be laid, like tiles, in a mortar bed; others are thicker, for bedding in sand with a hired plate vibrator (page 81). Paving bricks come in assorted colours and in dozens of shapes and sizes, including squares, hexagons and special interlocking forms.

At most builders' merchants, bricks are priced by the thousand, but they are least costly to buy in pre-packaged cubes of 500 to 1,000 bricks. Buying by the cube is not only more economical, but it also ensures that all your bricks are approximately the same colour and size. Small irregularities are inevitable, but these may even enhance the attractiveness of a wall or patio.

To estimate how many bricks you will need, first calculate in square metres the total area that needs to be covered. If the area is irregular, divide it into squares, rectangles or circles so that you can use standard arithmetical formulae for each segment, and then add up the segments. If you need a double layer of bricks—as in many walls—do not forget to allow for both surface areas.

Calculate the number of bricks you will require to cover a square metre as follows. For unmortared paving, multiply the length by width (in fractions of metres) of the brick surface that will be visible to work out the area in square metres. For mortared paving, walls and brick-sheathed steps, add 0.01 metres to each dimension before multiplying, to allow for the space taken up by the mortar between bricks.

Next, compute the brick quantity by multiplying the number of square metres in the area to be covered by the number of mortarless, or mortared, bricks to a square metre. Finally, add at least 5 per cent for cutting and breakage.

To estimate mortar requirements for paving, figure about 0.02 cubic metres for each square metre of bricks. For a double-thick wall, reckon about 0.05 cubic metres of mortar for each square metre of bricks, and for brick-veneered steps, about 0.03 cubic metres for each square metre. A 10 mm thick mortar bed for paving, walls or steps will require 0.01 cubic metres of mortar for each square metre.

Before ordering bricks, clear a generous delivery space close to the street or drive and as near as possible to the site where you plan to work. Build there a pallet or wood platform of boards. After the load is delivered, cover it with plastic sheeting.

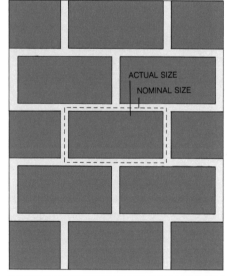

Brick sizes. Builders' merchants and bricklayers occasionally refer to a brick by its nominal rather than its actual size (dotted lines), which is the size as measured after it has been mortared into a wall with 10 mm for the mortar joint included. However, bricks are also specified in actual sizes. Both measurements represent only an average, in any case, as bricks from the same lot may vary in size by as much as 3 per cent.

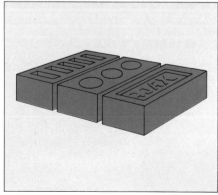

Solid and cored bricks. Some bricks are solid blocks, flat on all surfaces or with a slight depression—a frog—and the manufacturer's imprint on one side. However, some have rectangular or round holes called cores, which run through the bricks from top to bottom (two bricks on the left).

Cored bricks produce stronger walls because some of the mortar will trickle down into the holes; the tops of walls made with them must, of course, be covered with solid bricks. Paving bricks do not have cores, but you can use cored facing bricks instead for paths and patios wherever the pattern you have selected calls for bricks to be set on their sides or ends.

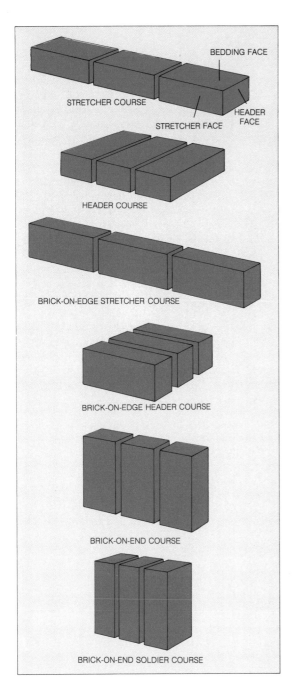

STRETCHER COURSE

BEDDING FACE

STRETCHER FACE

HEADER FACE

HEADER COURSE

BRICK-ON-EDGE STRETCHER COURSE

BRICK-ON-EDGE HEADER COURSE

BRICK-ON-END COURSE

BRICK-ON-END SOLDIER COURSE

Bricklayers' jargon. The names applied to positions of bricks and arrangements of rows come from terms for brick surfaces: the long sides are called stretcher faces, the ends header faces, the tops and bottoms bedding faces. When bricks are laid on bedding faces with the header faces abutting, the stretcher faces are exposed and the row is a stretcher course. When laid on bedding faces with the stretcher faces abutting, the header faces are exposed and the row is a header course. Bricks laid on stretcher faces form a brick-on-edge stretcher course when header faces abut, a brick-on-edge header course when bedding faces abut. Bricks laid on header faces form a brick-on-end course when stretcher faces abut, a brick-on-end soldier course when bedding faces abut.

The Popular Types

Dragged brick. This gives walls a rustic look and paving a practical surface. Bricks may be vertically or horizontally dragged, and the texture may be coarse or fine.

Smooth brick. Untextured on one side and both ends, it is useful for paving and walls.

Stippled brick. Roughly mottled on one side and both ends, this makes distinctive walls, but may be too uneven for paving.

Combed brick. Striped with deep grooves on one side and the ends, combed bricks form handsome walls. They may be horizontally or vertically combed.

Sandfaced brick. Grit, impregnated on one side and both ends, makes this texture suitable for non-slip paving and is attractive in walls. Sandfaced bricks are available in different degrees of coarseness.

Sandcreased brick. Textured on both sides as well as the ends, the sandcreased type looks hand-made and is used in walls.

Laying Bricks to Walk On

Bricks will produce an attractive and rugged path or patio if you simply lay them directly into the ground. Traffic, however, will shift the bricks out of place, and frosts will heave them up and break them. For more permanent paving, your best bet is to set the bricks into a bed of sand, or to lay them in mortar over a concrete foundation.

The chief advantages of brick paving are its handsome appearance and ease of construction—a child can help. However, unless the crevices between bricks are tightly mortared or filled with sand, they sprout weeds and catch toes and heels; brick paving is also prone to icing.

The six classic patterns for laying bricks are shown on the right. All the variations shown on the opposite page are based on these six patterns. An identical number of bricks is required to pave the same area with any of the classic patterns or the variations. Some more complicated patterns require cutting bricks into segments, and when you stand bricks on edge rather than lay them flat you will need half as many again to pave a prescribed area.

A plain pattern such as stack bond will serve well for small spaces since the design becomes clear after the first few rows are set out. More intricate patterns such as herring-bone and basket weave are better when you are paving a larger area since several pattern repeats are required before the design reveals itself clearly. The bricks required for all but the stack bond pattern must be approximately twice as long in actual length as they are wide.

The pattern you choose will also affect the resistance of the paving to shifting. Stack bond and basket weave have the least resistance because they incorporate continuous joints in both directions; herring-bone, with no continuous joints in either direction, is the strongest. In order to create a strong bond, many paving bricks are manufactured in interlocking shapes that dictate the pattern you can form.

To make sure your choice of patterns will work out as imagined, draw your path or patio area to scale before you even order bricks. Cut out miniature paper or cardboard rectangles of the size of your bricks and experiment with different combinations on your scale drawing.

The Basic Paving Patterns

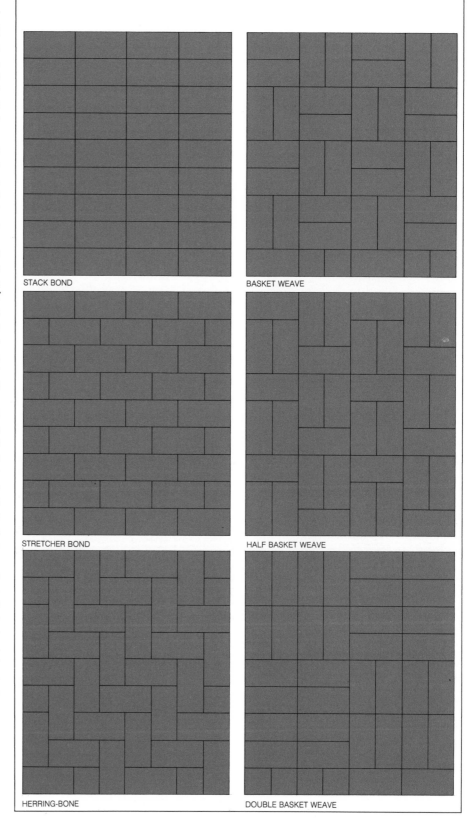

STACK BOND

BASKET WEAVE

STRETCHER BOND

HALF BASKET WEAVE

HERRING-BONE

DOUBLE BASKET WEAVE

Some Paving Variations

Shifting a pattern diagonally. Arrange your pattern repeats to fit diagonally, rather than perpendicularly, against the outside edges of your path or patio. Cut some of the bricks at an angle to fill the ends of each course.

Standing bricks on edge. By turning all of the bricks in any pattern on their sides, you get a lighter, more delicate-looking effect than when the bricks are laid flat. However, you will also need about 50 per cent more bricks to cover the area. To use bricks edgewise in a basket weave or herring-bone pattern, select bricks whose thickness is about one-third of their length.

Shifting the joints. A variation on a stretcher bond places the joints of the bricks in even rows at the one-third or one-quarter point of the bricks in odd rows, rather than at the conventional one-half mark. You can also use two or three different fractional variations for successive rows.

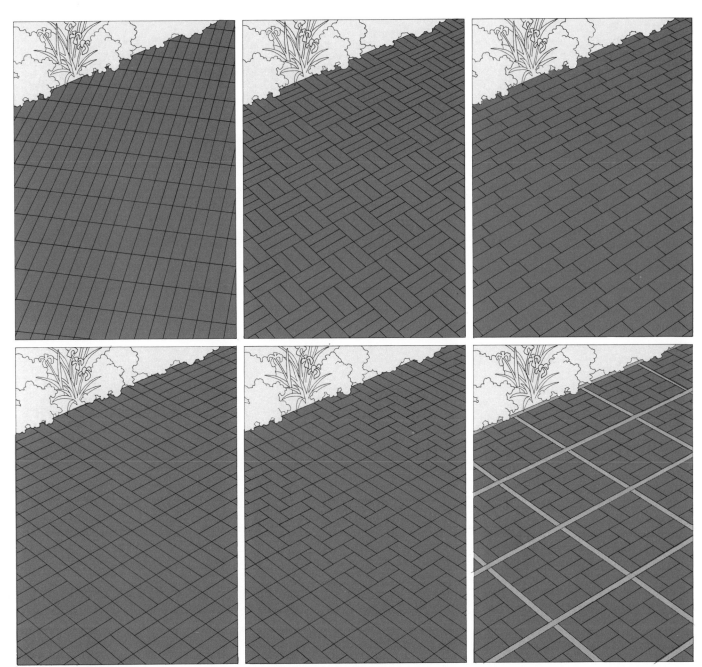

Changing directions. When two units of stack bond are set at right angles to each other, a simple pattern becomes more dramatic.

Combining patterns. For large areas, you can vary the paving by mixing together two or even three patterns. In the drawing above, a fancy herring-bone alternates with a plain stack bond. If you try to combine two complicated patterns, one may detract from the other.

Gridding patterns. For structural strength, build grids made from preservative-treated timber or precast-concrete garden edging strips into the path or patio. The patterns within the grids may be identical or may differ from grid to grid.

Classic Paths to Modern Paving

The methods for covering level surfaces with brick have not changed much over the last 5,000 years, though they have been put to some new uses. The techniques used by generations of builders to lay brick pavements and courtyards, for example, are now called upon for flower-bed borders and swimming-pool terraces. But the most common use of brick paving is still the construction of paths and patios, whether mortared or unmortared.

The brick used in these basic instructions is paving brick, which is manufactured in varying thicknesses—some substantially thinner than those of facing bricks—and in many non-standard shapes and sizes. You can achieve similar results with concrete units the size of standard bricks, commonly known as concrete paving blocks.

In frost-free regions and in firm soil, the bricks can be laid directly on the ground, but for a more stable and long-lasting surface they should be bedded in sand and checked for evenness with a spirit level. Even so, such bricks may have to be re-levelled every few years.

A more reliable way of bedding bricks without mortar is to use a hired plate vibrator *(page 81)*, which will produce level paving rigid enough to bear the weight of cars in drives. Plate vibrators should be used only with bricks at least 50 mm thick. Bricks levelled with a plate vibrator will need to be surrounded by edging bricks bedded in concrete *(Step 2, right)*. Unmortared surfaces bedded by hand can be edged with bricks supported by tamped earth alone.

Durable paving can also be ensured by laying bricks in a bed of mortar over concrete. The foundation may be old—an existing path or slab will do—or newly poured, following the instructions for constructing lightweight slabs. In either case, the job is best accomplished in two distinct steps: first bond the bricks to the slab with ordinary mortar, then fill the space between bricks with a stiff mortar once the initial layer has hardened.

Paving without Mortar

1 **Laying the dry run.** Measure and stake the area to be paved as you would for a concrete slab, then estimate the number of bricks by the method used for unmortared paving *(page 74)*. To establish the final spacing of the bricks and to dig the paving bed and edging trench to exact dimensions, lay out some bricks in a preliminary dry run. Enclose the entire area with edging bricks set on the ground, and lay out paving bricks within the edging. Allow for a 100 mm gap outside the edging bricks when setting out the borders of the paving. For a simple pattern like a stretcher bond, you can save time by laying out bricks along the sides of the area, leaving the middle bare, but be sure to complete the sides.

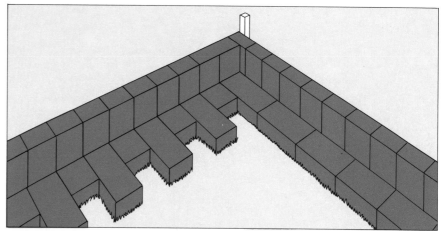

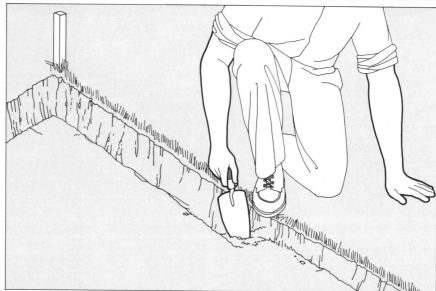

2 **Edging the bed.** Remove the bricks that you set out for the dry run and dig a bed 50 mm deeper than the thickness of the paving bricks. Follow the existing slope and keep the sides of the bed as nearly vertical as possible. Then, using a garden trowel, dig an edging trench—100 mm wider than the bricks and deep enough to accommodate 100 mm of concrete and enough of the bricks-on-end to leave their tops flush with the finished paving—along the inner borders of the bed. Lay a 100 mm thick strip of general-purpose concrete in the trench and bed the edging bricks into the concrete while it is still workable. They should form a level, upright wall that encloses the paving bed. Support the inner faces of the edging bricks with a straight length of timber while you fill the trench behind them two-thirds full of concrete. Replace the turf or soil and leave the concrete to cure for three days before proceeding.

Some Edging Variations

A line of bricks-on-end. The simplest of all brick edgings is a straight line of bricks set on end with the long, narrow stretcher faces abutting. A line of soldiers, with the wide bedding faces abutting, makes a sharper and more attractive contrast with the paving bricks—but it requires almost twice as many bricks.

A gentle curve. Curved brick for a curved edging is available, but expensive. You can get the same effect with common bricks by angling bricks-on-end to form a gentle curve and filling the narrow wedges between the bricks with strong mortar, following one of the recipes on page 12.

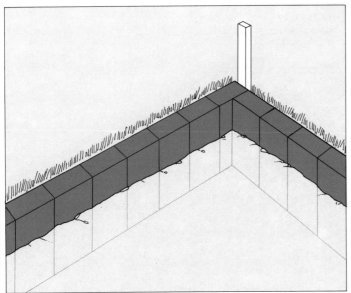

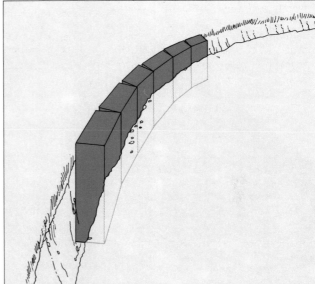

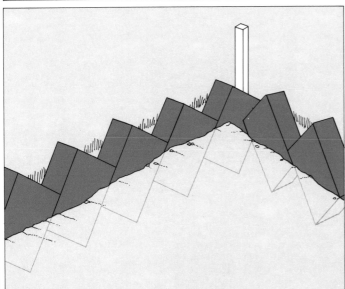

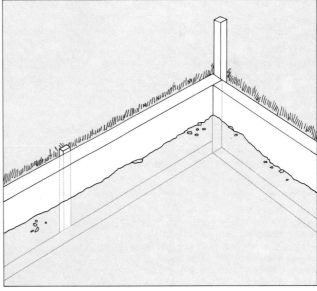

A sawtooth edging. Bricks-on-end tilted at an angle of 45 degrees create a provocative optical illusion; when the paving bricks are in place, the edging seems to consist of a row of triangular bricks neatly cut to size. To enhance the illusion, dig a slightly shallower bed and trench, so that the paving and edging bricks project above ground level. Caution: lay this edging with care—the bases of the bricks must be firmly embedded in concrete and the tops levelled.

A wood edging. The forms that are used for pouring concrete adapt readily to the bed-and-trench construction of brick paving. Conceal the edgings by setting their tops and supporting stakes at or slightly below ground level.

3 **Making the sand bed.** Tamp the earth of the bed, lay in a bed of sharp sand—the type used in mixing concrete—and level the sand. The sand bed must be set just far enough below the edging so that bricks laid on it will be roughly 10 mm above the edging before they are bedded with a plate vibrator. If you intend to bed the paving by hand, the bricks should be laid on the sand so that they are level with the edging. In a patio bed, set parallel wood strips on the earth about a metre apart, pour sand between them and work a third strip across their tops to smooth the sand, then remove the strips and fill in depressions. To level a bed for a path, use the method for levelling the sub-base for a concrete path *(page 49)*.

WOOD STRIP

LEVELLING BOARD

4 **Laying the bricks.** Work the first two paving bricks into a corner of the bed. With the first bricks in place, use a length of thin twine wrapped round two bricks to set the alignment for the entire course. Place the two bricks outside the edging with the twine flush to the inner sides of the bricks you have laid. Continue to lay bricks close together—the final course should finish within 10 mm of the edging.

If you are bedding the paving by hand, use a spirit level as you work to check for a perfectly flat surface from brick to brick. Tap bricks with a rubber mallet to level them and, if necessary, add or remove sand under individual bricks. Then skip to the instructions for finishing paving by hand *(opposite page, below)*.

5 Using a plate vibrator. Pass a petrol-powered plate vibrator—obtainable from a plant-hire agency—over the bricks two or three times to bed them firmly into the sand. They will settle about 10 mm, making them flush with the edging. Do not walk on the bricks before bedding them.

6 Filling the cracks. Spread a layer of sand thinly over the paving and make one or two more passes with the plate vibrator to completely fill the cracks. Have a helper brush the sand towards you as you work since the vibrations will tend to drive the sand away from the machine.

Finishing Paving by Hand

Sanding the cracks. When all the bricks have been laid and levelled, pour over the surface a bucket of sharp sand. Spread the sand backwards and forwards with your hand, or with a brush or a broom, in order to fill the cracks *(above, left)*. After all the cracks have been filled with sand, gently sweep any excess sand off, working at a diagonal to the cracks *(above, right)*—broom strokes parallel to the cracks are liable to brush out the top layer of sand. Sanding may have to be repeated after the first application has been settled.

Paving with Mortar

1 **Edging a concrete slab.** When covering an existing slab, be sure it is level and in good repair. If you pour a new slab, make one 100 mm thick, following the directions for unreinforced slabs and using general-purpose concrete. You need not edge a slab lying so far below the ground that the tops of the paving bricks will be at or near ground level. Otherwise, use edging to conceal the concrete and protect the outermost bricks from moisture and nicks.

Dig a trench round the slab, about twice as wide as the edging bricks-on-end and sufficiently deep to bring their tops flush with the level of the paving bricks. (In your calculations, add an extra 10 mm to the depth of the paving bricks to allow for the mortar bed.) Hose down the edging bricks thoroughly and set them into the trench on-end, flat sides facing out, using a forefinger or a 10 mm thick scrap of wood as a spacer to allow for mortaring between the bricks. Tamp concrete against the outside edge of the edging bricks to pin them to the concrete slab, and use a steel tape measure and a level to make certain that the bricks will rise above the slab to the combined thickness of the paving bricks and a 10 mm bed joint.

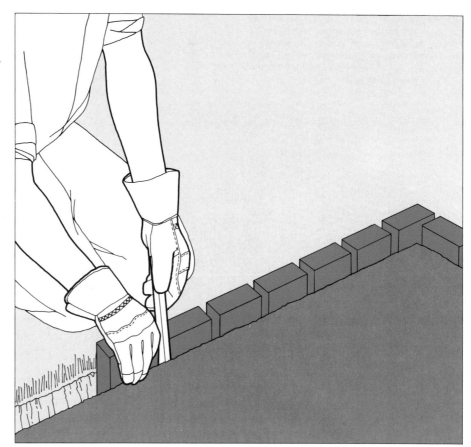

2 **Preparing the bed joints.** Lay out paving bricks in a dry run to determine their fit along the width and length of the slab, leaving 10 mm spaces for mortar joints on all sides of each brick. If necessary, reduce or enlarge the spacing to improve the fit. You can leave some of the dry run in place as you work, serving as a guide to the placement of the mortared bricks.

Mix strong mortar (following one of the recipes on page 12) in batches of 0.02 cubic metres to cover about 2 square metres of the slab with a 10 mm thick bed joint. If the total area to be paved is less than 4 square metres, you can mix extra mortar for the entire bed joint. Otherwise, observe the 0.02 cubic metre limit, which yields no more mortar than you can easily cover in an hour, when it will begin to harden. Smooth and level the mortar, then use a notched trowel or the point of a bricklayer's trowel to score it.

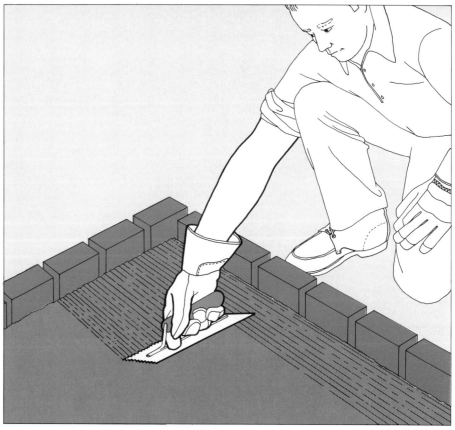

3 Laying the bricks. Soak the bricks thoroughly, then set them in place on the bed joint, smooth face up, using a stretched length of twine as a guide. Lay one complete course across the slab before starting the next. Position individual bricks by pushing them into the bed joint and tapping them lightly with the handle of the trowel; use a level to check that there is a flat surface from brick to brick.

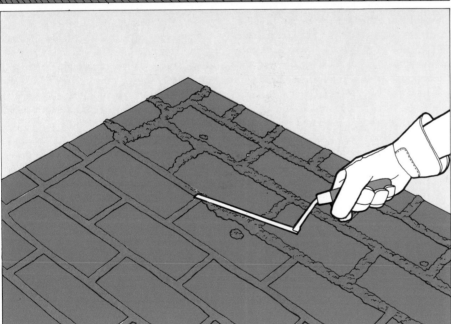

4 Mortaring the joints. At least a day—preferably two or three—after you lay the paving bricks on the mortar bed, mix a batch of stiff mortar to fill the joints between the bricks, using the formula on page 74 to determine the quantity. The mixture should be drier than the mortar normally used for building with bricks. Mix 1 part Portland cement with 3 parts soft sand and add very little water. The mortar should barely hold together when squeezed into a ball.

Dampen the bricks and work the stiff mortar into the joints with a small trowel or a brick jointer. Use the jointer or a piece of wood to tamp the mortar to the bottom of the joint. When the mortar nears the top of the bricks, use the full width of the tool to press down on the joints and fill gaps. Mortar until the joint overflows slightly. Use a trowel to shift or remove excess mortar, making sure that no mortar is left on the surface of the bricks. Rub the joints smooth and recess them by 1 to 2 mm to provide channels for draining rainwater, using a stiff brush or a small sand-filled hessian bag. Wipe mortar smears from the bricks with a damp sponge and dampen the paving with a hose-pipe set to a fine spray. Leave to set for a day or two.

The Basics of Building with Blocks: a Brick Wall

Not everyone can match the expertise of Sir Winston Churchill, an amateur brick-layer who could lay a brick a minute (the average beginner's rate is often half this speed) and was invited to join the bricklayers' union. But anyone who wants to can lay bricks well, in structures that are both useful and good-looking. The work is not difficult—bricks are light and easy to handle, and their uniform size makes planning and patterning surprisingly simple. The finished structure can range from a free-standing wall made of brick alone to a complex affair—a flight of stairs or an outdoor barbecue, for instance—consisting of an inexpensive block core with a handsome brick veneer covering. The free-standing wall, lending charm to the smallest garden or enclosing spaces such as flower beds and play areas, is probably the most common and the most popular. You can build your own—a wall standing on a concrete footing and rising up to 1.2 metres high—by using the techniques that are shown in the illustrations on the following pages.

The planning of a brick-construction job begins when you choose a location, well before the first brick is laid. For the brick wall, start by consulting the local building and planning regulations, your neighbours and (if you do not own the property) your landlord, to be sure there are no legal obstacles to your proposed wall. Next, check the firmness of your soil; the best-built wall may buckle or sink if it rests on marshy or spongy ground. Study the exact site of the wall with special care. A hill or slope presents special difficulties; avoid large trees with thick and widespread roots; and make sure that the concrete footing of the wall, which will extend by the width of a brick to the front and rear, will not overlap an adjacent property line or path.

Now plan the wall itself in detail. To avoid the complexities of reinforcement, you should keep the wall under 1.2 metres high, but you can make it up to 6 metres long and shape it with square corners. You can choose among a number of pattern bonds—that is, different ways of interlocking the bricks—but you are probably best off with the simplest pattern, called stretcher bond, in which the bricks overlap one another so that vertical joints are staggered from course to course. (The basic wall shown on the following pages is laid in stretcher bond.)

When you have decided upon the size and shape of the wall, estimate the amount of materials you will need and bring them to the site all at once. A 250 by 400 mm concrete footing contains 0.1 cubic metres of concrete for each metre of its length. To determine the number of bricks, multiply the length of the wall by its height and double this figure (because the finished wall will be two bricks thick) to give the surface area of the wall in square metres. Then multiply this figure by 60, the number of standard-sized bricks in a square metre of a wall. Calculate the amount of mortar required on the basis of about 0.05 cubic metres for each square metre of wall surface.

When you place your order with a builders' merchant, select bricks that are roughly twice as long as they are wide, so that the topmost course, when placed across the parallel rows of bricks below it, will cover them completely. Be sure to check that the supplier has a stock of the same bricks readily available—bricks are often delivered broken or chipped, and you may spoil more bricks than you expect if you have to split any.

When you have completed the footing, let the concrete harden for a day or two before going on to bricklaying. As you work, set separate piles of bricks at convenient points to save time, and keep a bucket of clean water or a hose handy nearby to clean your trowel and your spirit level. Wet down the completed wall, and keep it moist for several days until the mortar has cured. After two weeks or so, clean off any areas of efflorescence that may have developed on the bricks' surface *(page 37)*.

Making a Gauge Rod

To control the heights of courses in any brick structure, the best tool to use is a measuring stick called a gauge rod, which can easily be made at home. For a brick wall, cut a piece of scrap timber to the total planned height of the wall. With a laundry marker or a similar indelible marker, draw a line near one end of the rod to indicate the top of the bricks in the first course. This first mark on the rod should be equal to the combined height of a 10 mm mortar bed plus the exact height of a single brick. Then mark the brick height and mortar bed of each successive course all the way up the rod. As you build the wall, set the rod against newly laid bricks to make sure that the courses of brick rise evenly at every point.

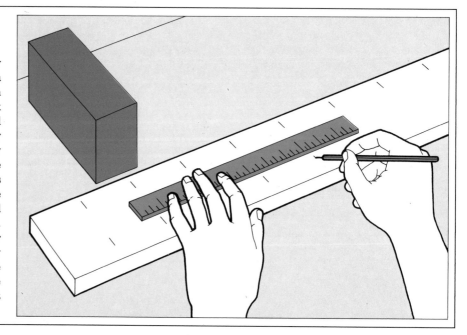

The anatomy of a brick wall. A free-standing brick wall, shown here in cross-section, is actually a combination of simple structures. Like all walls, it rests on a footing—in this case, a poured concrete slab 250 mm deep and 400 mm wide. The top of the footing is 100 mm below ground level to allow soil for planting to be placed next to the edge of the wall. Some walls consist of a single row of bricks; for added strength and better proportions, this one has two parallel rows, separated by a narrow air space and bound together at regular intervals by metal strips called wall ties. Both rows are formed by stretcher courses—bricks placed end to end, with 10 mm thick mortar joints. At the top, the rows are locked together by a coping of bricks set on edge—bricks set on their long narrow sides and extending from the front of the wall to the back.

COPING

100 mm

250 mm

400 mm

The Plan

A dry run for the first courses. From a fixed horizontal reference line, such as the side of your house, drive or property line, measure out the baseline you have chosen for the face, or front, of the wall. Drive stakes at the ends of this line and stretch a string between them. Then lay out the first face course of bricks on the ground between the stakes, following the string as a guide and using a piece of wood to make 10-mm gaps between bricks. If the end bricks do not quite reach the stakes or fall slightly beyond them, move the stakes to fit the bricks.

Begin the rear, or back-up, course of bricks about 10 mm behind the face course. When you have placed several bricks, set a brick on edge across the parallel rows; if it does not fit exactly across the width of the bricks, adjust the width of the space between front and back courses. Lay out the remaining back-up bricks.

The Footing

Building and marking the footing. Mark the baseline on the ground with sand *(page 43)* and use it as a guide for a trench about 350 mm deep. The trench must be long and wide enough to extend beyond the wall by about half the wall's thickness—the thickness of a single brick—in every direction. In this wall, the bricks are just over 100 mm thick, so the trench should extend about 100 mm beyond each end of the baseline, and should be about 400 mm wide, overlapping the baseline about 100 mm in front and 300 mm behind. Mix foundation concrete *(page 26)* and pour the footing to 100 mm below ground level. In the final smoothing, taper the edges of the concrete downwards very slightly—no more than 5 mm—to provide a runoff for excess moisture. Finally, mark the baseline again, 100 mm from the front of the footing, with a chalk line *(below)*.

CHALK LINE

100 mm

The Lead

1 Laying the first bricks. Dampen about 25 bricks with a hose-pipe set at a fine spray, then let the surface moisture evaporate. (Follow this procedure each time you use more bricks.) Mix 0.01 cubic metres of mortar *(page 12)*. Clean away loose dirt from the top of the footing and moisten about a metre of the surface at one end of the foundation with the hose set to a fine spray and let this surface moisture evaporate. Throw a mortar line just behind the chalk line and lay three bricks on the mortar bed *(pages 13 and 14)*. These first bricks will begin to form the lead, or end of the wall.

To make sure that the bricks exactly follow the chalk line, align a level from the bricks to the chalk line beyond them. Adjust the bricks, if necessary, to make them perfectly straight and flush to the chalk line. Set a gauge rod beside the bricks at various points to be sure that the bed joint measures 10 mm; the top of the brick should align with the first mark on the rod. (Repeat these checks with the gauge rod as you lay each course of brick.)

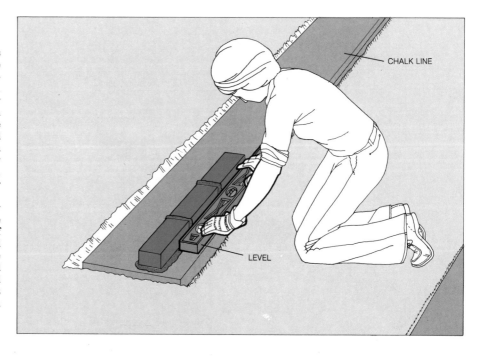

CHALK LINE

LEVEL

2 **Starting the back-up course.** Throw a mortar line parallel to the three bricks you have laid for the face course and about 10 mm behind them. Place a brick at the end of the mortar line, 10 mm behind the first face brick—or at the spacing determined in your dry run—and continue the back-up course with two stretcher bricks. Use a level to align the back-up bricks, and set it across both courses at several points to be sure that the front and back bricks are level with each other.

Start the second course of face and back-up bricks, beginning with a header brick laid across the first course from back to front. (As the wall rises, alternate courses are started with a header brick.) Lay two stretcher bricks on each course, to form a step up from the first to second course; these steps will run to the top of the lead.

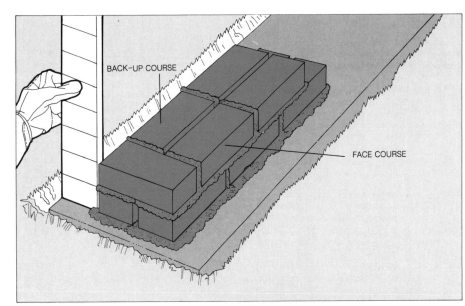

BACK-UP COURSE

FACE COURSE

3 **Placing the first ties.** Wall ties are placed along the wall on top of the second course and all other even-numbered courses. Throw mortar lines on the second courses and embed ties in the mortar about 450 mm apart *(right)* by gently pushing them into the mortar with the tip of the trowel. Then lay two stretcher bricks over the embedded ties to begin the third face and back-up courses.

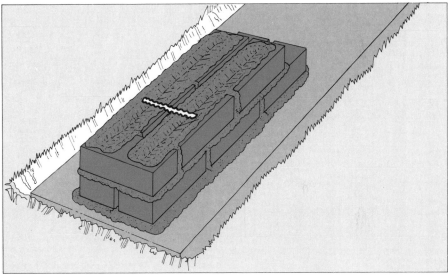

Wall Ties for Strength

Metal wall ties, inserted at regular intervals in a double-thick wall, help to hold the two courses together and so increase the strength of the structure. They may not be necessary when crosswise header bricks are incorporated into the bonding pattern. But in walls laid in a stretcher bond pattern, such as the one shown here, header bricks are only used at the beginning and end of alternate courses, and wall ties must be mortared into the bedding joints as bricklaying proceeds, to tie the face and back-up courses together.

Wall ties are usually made of galvanized steel, to prevent rusting, and come in several shapes. They may be crimped steel strips *(above)*, steel wire in the shape of a butterfly or the letter Z, or flat steel strips twisted in the middle and forked at each end (known as "fish tails").

Wall ties should be set at regular intervals of 450 mm horizontally (corresponding to every second stretcher brick) and 150 mm vertically (corresponding to alternate courses). Lay wall ties across the quarter points of stretcher bricks rather than in the middle of the bricks directly above vertical joints, and stagger them so that each tie lies half way between those on the alternate course below.

4 **Completing the first lead.** Lay five courses of the face and back-up, with wall ties between the fourth and fifth courses; the lead should now be stepped up to a single brick at the end of each course. Use the level to check alignment. If you find a protruding brick, tap the level with your trowel handle to push the brick back into line. If a brick recedes, tap it from behind to bring it flush to the level. Do not worry about minute irregularities; correct only those that are obtrusive.

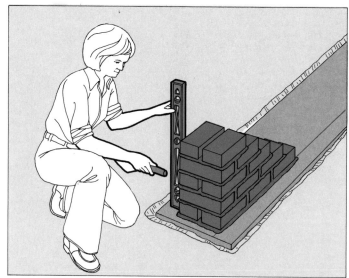

5 **Building the opposite lead.** At the opposite end of the footing, repeat Steps 1 to 4 to form a five-course lead. Checks with the gauge rod and the level are especially important at this stage of the job. The two leads must match each other exactly; if they do not, the completed wall will be unstable, with no way to correct the problem short of tearing down the leads and starting afresh.

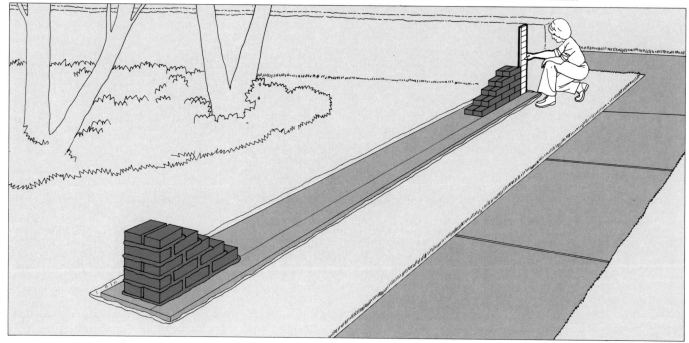

Joining the Leads

1 **Preparing a guide line.** When laying bricks between the leads, use a guide line—a string, slightly longer than the wall, stretched between wood or plastic blocks. If your supplier does not stock such blocks, make them from pieces of wood. Tie a length of nylon or other synthetic string round a block, then fit it into the lengthwise groove.

Hook the block round the end brick in the first course, aligning the string precisely to the top edge of the brick. Extend the line to the other end of the wall, fasten the string to the second block, and hook this block round the corresponding brick in the first course; as before, the string should be flush with the top edge of the brick.

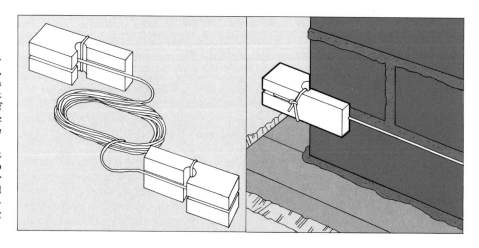

2 **Laying bricks between the leads.** Working from the ends of the wall towards the middle, lay the first face course between the leads, using the taut line as a guide; the line should be a millimetre or two in front of the bricks and flush with the top edges. At the centre, place a closure brick, buttering both ends. Then lay the first back-up course, using the line at the back of the wall.

3 **Building up to the top of the leads.** Always working from the ends towards the middle of the wall, lay the next four face and back-up courses. Move the guide line up one course at a time and insert wall ties about every 450 mm on top of the second and fourth courses. When you have inserted closure bricks in the last course, the wall will be approximately 375 mm high—depending on the size of the bricks. If you wish to complete it at this point, lay a coping of bricks on edge *(page 90)* and fill the joints between end bricks of the two parallel rows with mortar.

4 **Extending the wall upwards.** If you want a higher wall, build new five-course leads at the ends and fill in the courses between the leads, always working from the ends towards the middle. As before, use a gauge rod when building up the two leads and a guide line for the bricks between them. These five additional courses give a wall about 750 mm high; a third set of five courses makes it about 1.125 metres high. One more course of brick—making 16—raises the wall to a maximum practical height of 1.2 metres.

The Coping

1 Planning the job. When you have raised the wall to the height you have chosen, cap it with a coping of bricks laid on edge across the wall from front to back. Set the course out dry, with gaps for 10 mm mortar joints between the bricks. If the last brick extends beyond, or falls short of, the end of the wall by only a centimetre or two, adjust the mortar joints between the other coping bricks accordingly and measure the width of the adjusted joints. If the fit is not close enough to make this feasible, remove the last brick and, allowing for a 10 mm joint, measure the distance from the preceding brick to the edge of the wall. Mark a cutting line round the last brick at this distance, then score and split it lengthwise. Place the split brick on the wall to be sure that the fit is precise, then remove all the bricks.

BRICKS-ON-EDGE

SPLIT BRICK HERE

PARTIAL BRICK

2 Laying the bricks. Mix a small batch of mortar for the coping, following either of the strong recipes on page 12. Starting at one end of the wall, throw mortar lines on the top face and back-up course to set the first brick on edge at the end of the wall; then butter one side of the next brick with enough mortar to cover the side completely, and lay this brick. Measure this and all succeeding joints to be sure that the course matches the dry run. Continue laying bricks on edge along the wall. Because three bricks on edge correspond roughly to one stretcher brick, you must make some end-on-end joints, called jack joints, at the end of stretcher bricks; in this case, they will not affect wall strength. If you have cut a partial brick for the coping, lay whole bricks on edge to within three or four bricks of the end of the wall.

3 Completing the coping. Insert the partial brick at this point near the end of the wall, to make it less obvious in the finished course, then lay the remaining bricks. When you have placed the last brick, hold it in place for several minutes until the mortar hardens slightly. Then check the entire course with a level to be sure that each brick is perfectly aligned in all directions.

A Wall with Corners

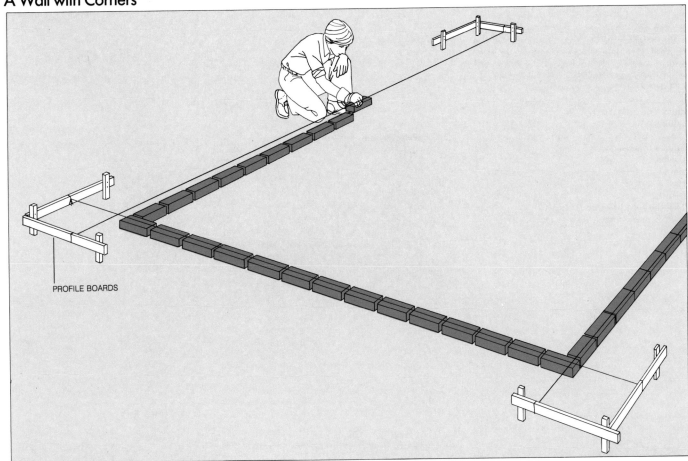

PROFILE BOARDS

1 **Planning the wall.** Determine the shape of the wall and establish a base line for the most prominent section. Then, following the procedure given for a straight wall, lay out the face course for this section with dry bricks. Form the beginnings of corners with single bricks set at right angles to the main section, using a carpenter's steel square to set the angles temporarily.

As guidelines for the concrete footings, set up profile boards at the corners and ends of the wall and use the 3-4-5 triangle method *(page 65)* to align the profile board strings flush to the front of the face courses and intersecting at the corners. Use a plumb line to be sure that the intersections of the strings fall directly above the points you have chosen for the corners; readjust the strings if necessary. Then plumb the points for the ends of the wall and mark the strings with chalk or coloured fabric to indicate both the lines of the wall and a point equal to half the width of the finished wall beyond them for the lines of the footing. Lay the sides of the wall dry *(above)*, fitting the bricks precisely; then remove the bricks and mark the profile board strings on the ground by pouring sand over the strings as a guide for the position of the trench for the footing. Mark the position of the strings on the profile boards and take away the strings, leaving the profile boards in place.

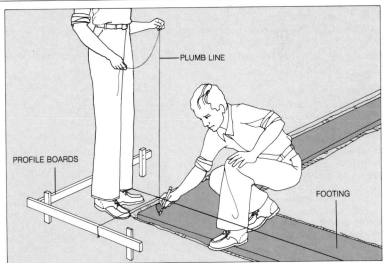

PLUMB LINE

PROFILE BOARDS

FOOTING

2 **Marking the footing.** Dig a trench and pour concrete for the footing, with the surface 100 mm below ground level. Leave the concrete to harden overnight, then replace the profile board strings and drop plumb lines to mark the footings at the corners *(above)* and the ends of the wall. On each section of the footing, stretch and snap a chalk line between each of the marks to indicate the position for the face course of bricks.

3 **Forming the corner.** Throw two mortar lines at one of the corners, on the foundation, just inside the chalk lines. Lay brick A *(right)* on the corner, then butter and lay brick B, using a steel square to check that the bricks form a right angle. Lay the four bricks beyond the corner in the order shown—C, D, E and F—to make a six-brick corner lead, and check with a level to be sure the bricks are flush with the chalk line.

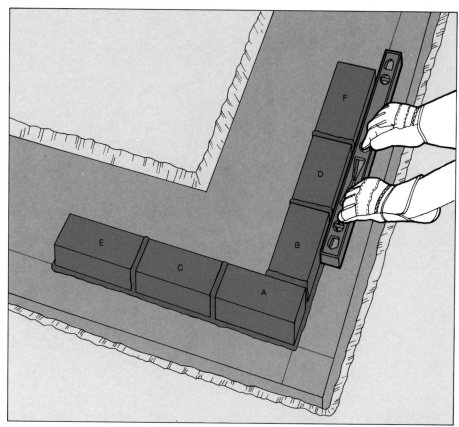

4 **Starting the back-up lead.** Throw mortar lines behind the face course, and lay the first three bricks of the back-up course *(right)* far enough behind the face course to make a perfect fit for the coping of bricks on edge. The back-up bricks must form a right angle and lie parallel to the face bricks; use the gauge rod to measure the height of this and succeeding courses.

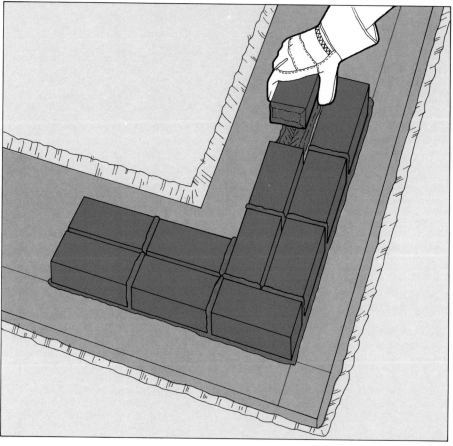

5 Completing the leads. Working on the front and back-up courses simultaneously, build up the corner lead to a height of five courses, with the ends of each course stepped down from the corner. Then build the corresponding corner and end leads or, if you plan to have only one corner, the ends leads alone. Stretch a guide line between the corners—or between a corner and an end—and fill in the bricks between the leads. If you want a wall higher than five courses, add corner and end leads and lay bricks between them until you reach the required height.

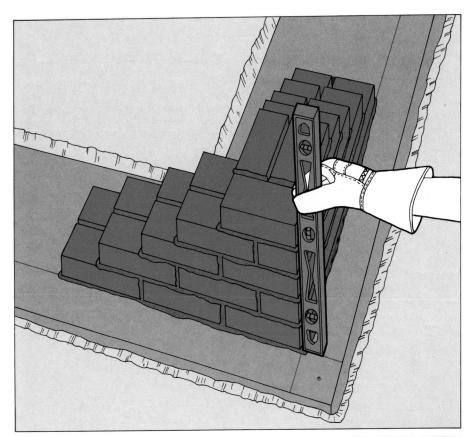

6 Laying the coping. Starting at a front corner of the wall, lay dry bricks on edge to determine the correct fit of the coping. If necessary, split a brick at the end. Lay this row of bricks as you would for a straight wall, with a partial brick inserted three or four bricks from the end, if necessary. Then lay the bricks on edge for the other side or sides of the wall, as shown on the right. Continue until the wall is completed. Cover and cure the completed wall, wait several weeks, then clean off all mortar stains and efflorescence.

Paving with Concrete Slabs

Paving slabs provide a simple and speedy alternative to pouring concrete or laying paving bricks for a path or patio. Most are between 40 and 60 mm thick, and shaped into squares or rectangles, although hexagons are also available. Typically, square slabs are sold in 225 and 450 mm sizes. Besides the standard grey shade, concrete slabs are sold in a variety of colours, from beige to shades of red and green, and in several finishes—they may be smooth or ribbed, and some reproduce the effect of natural stone but at a fraction of the cost.

You can save both time and effort by planning the design of your paving to use only whole slabs. If that is not possible and you must cut slabs to size, follow the instructions on page 103 for trimming flagstones. When estimating how many slabs you need, allow a few extra for wastage, especially if you need to trim or cut any units. When the slabs are delivered, stack them on their edges on timber battens to keep the edges clean and undamaged.

On firm, sandy soils, paving slabs can be laid directly on mortar. Start by excavating the area to a depth equal to the thickness of the slabs plus 25 mm for the mortar bed, so that the path will be flush with the ground. Level and compact the soil with a garden roller. On clayey or peaty soils, however, you will need to make your excavation 100 mm deeper, to allow for a 75 mm thick sub-base of crushed stone or hoggin topped with 25 mm of raked and rolled sand. Bed the slabs on the sand using the spot mortar technique shown on the right.

Before you lay any slabs, cut 10 mm thick spacers from scrap timber or plywood. These will be used to maintain consistent joint spaces between slabs. You will need to place two spacers in each joint, removing them as the slabs are laid.

1 Throwing the mortar bed. Mix a wheelbarrowful of strong mortar—about 0.05 cubic metres—following one of the recipes given on page 12. Start at one corner of the path or patio and lay mortar for one slab at a time. For each slab, throw three strips of mortar about 75 mm wide and 50 mm thick along the length of the area that is to be covered by the slab *(right)*. Keep the edges of the mortar strips about 25 mm within the area which the slab will cover, in order to allow room for the mortar to spread when the slab is laid in position. Slabs whose smallest dimension is 225 mm or less will need only two strips of mortar.

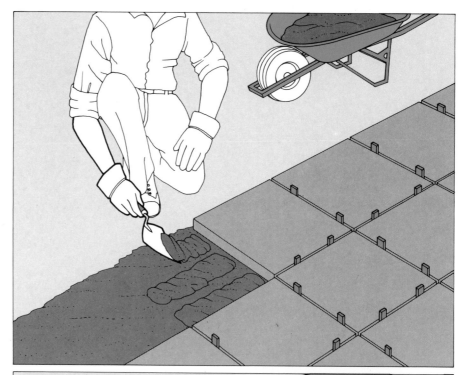

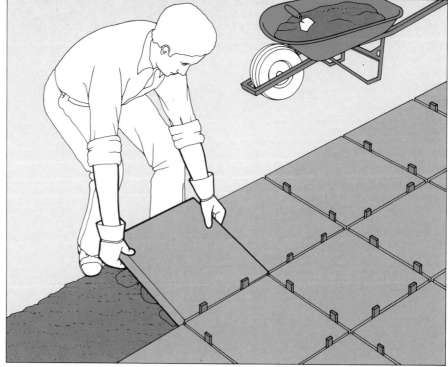

2 Placing the slab. Before lowering each slab into place, position two spacers in the two adjacent joints. Push each spacer firmly into the mortar so that it is touching the next slab. Lower the slab that you are laying carefully so that its edges rest against the spacers. Remove any mortar smears from the slab with a damp sponge.

3 **Levelling the slab.** Use a spirit level and a straight-edge long enough to span two or three slabs to level the slabs, adding or removing mortar as necessary. As you lay each slab, tap it with a rubber or wooden mallet until it is firmly bedded and does not rock. Remove the spacers from the joints before the mortar sets.

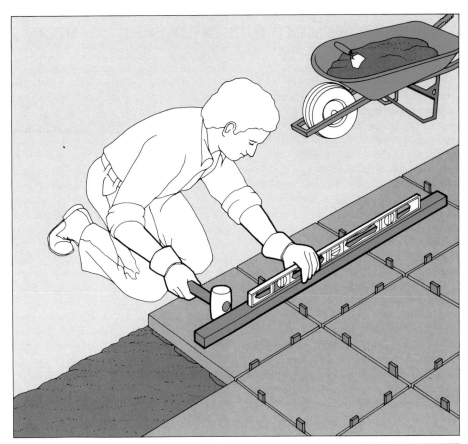

4 **Filling the joints.** At least a day—preferably two or three—after you lay the slabs, mix a batch of stiff mortar to fill the joints between the slabs. Mix 1 part Portland cement with 3 parts soft sand and add very little water, so that the mortar barely holds together when squeezed into a ball. Pack mortar into the joints with a trowel or a length of flat metal bar until the joints overflow slightly. Use a trowel to remove excess mortar, making sure that none is left on the surface of the slabs. Rub the joints smooth and recess them by 1 or 2 mm to provide channels for draining rainwater, using a stiff brush or a rounded piece of metal. Wipe any remaining mortar smears from the slabs with a damp sponge. Let the mortar set for a day or two before using the path.

Veneering a Concrete Slab with Ceramic Tiles

An elegant way to finish a concrete path or patio is to cover it with a veneer of unglazed ceramic tiles. Made of strong and durable fired clay, they differ from bathroom wall tiles because they do not have a shiny surface glaze, which would make them very slippery underfoot.

To ensure a professional-looking job when veneering with tiles, you must start with a perfectly smooth slab. Since you will lay the tiles in mortar no more than 20 mm thick, variations greater than 10 mm can not be accommodated in an existing slab, or the tiles will tilt up and down across the surface. Even hairline cracks in the concrete may cause the tiles to work loose.

If you are pouring a new slab, follow the instructions on pages 42–53, using general-purpose concrete. Construct expansion and control joints as you would for an ordinary slab, and reinforce it if necessary. Do not make the finish of a new concrete slab too smooth—a slightly rough surface will provide a better key for the mortar bed. A new slab need not be allowed to cure completely before tiles are laid—in fact, the mortar will adhere better if you begin to lay tiles as soon as the concrete is hard enough not to be marked.

Check the surface of the slab for smoothness with a long straightedge. Lie on the slab and look under the straightedge for slits of light, indicating bumps or dips in the surface, and outline areas where the irregularity is more than 5 to 10 mm with a crayon or chalk. Then, wearing goggles, flatten any high spots with an abrasive disc attached to a power drill. Fill or repair depressions, large cracks or spalled patches following the instructions on pages 20–21, levelling large patches with a straightedge. Then hose the concrete clean.

Forming the mortar bed, as shown in the cross-section opposite, is a three-step operation that has to be completed without any delays. A paper-thin layer of cement slurry, or skim coat, is applied with the smooth side of a box-notch trowel; over the skim coat then goes a 20 mm mortar top coat, which finally is raked with the notched side of the trowel to form ridges of uniform thickness. Seat tiles in the mortar with uniform joint spaces between 6 and 9 mm wide. After the mortar cures, put ceramic tile grout into all spaces except those located above expansion joints, which are filled in with mineral wool or strips of foam and ordinary caulking.

Two types of tile come in unglazed versions suitable for outdoor use: mosaic and quarry tiles. The mosaic tiles, which are laid slightly differently from quarry tiles, are small, between 20 and 75 mm across, usually 5 to 10 mm thick, and come mounted in groups on rectangles of paper or mesh. Quarry tiles are most often square, but are also available in rectangular or oblong shapes, in which case the longest dimension ranges from 50 to 250 mm. Typically, square tiles measure 150 by 150 mm or 200 by 200 mm; for outdoor use they should be at least 8 mm thick. Various anti-slip finishes—among them, studded, ribbed or rough textured—are available; such tiles are recommended for locations likely to be exposed to frost. Some tiles incorporate projecting lugs round the edges to make it easier to achieve a uniform joint width, and the top edges of many quarry tiles are slightly chamfered to form a smooth surface that is suitable for floors over which chairs must slide.

How tiles stand up outdoors depends not on size or type but on water absorption. If water penetrates a tile and freezes inside, the tile cracks. Only unglazed tiles with a water absorption rating under 2 per cent—your local supplier should have the manufacturer's specifications that show the figure—can be safely used outdoors in cold climates.

Mosaics are generally packaged in cartons containing 300 mm square sheets; quarry tiles in cartons containing sufficient tiles to cover either ½ or 1 square metre. Most suppliers will split cartons to suit your requirements, but some will only sell whole packs. To estimate your needs, multiply the length of the area that you want to cover by the width (treating an L-shaped area as two rectangles) and add 5 per cent for waste. If you overestimate your requirements, some suppliers will give a refund for any unused sheets or unopened cartons of tiles.

For laying ceramic tiles outdoors, you need about 0.02 cubic metres of mortar for each square metre of 200 by 200 mm tiles. Ceramic tile grout, which is available in colours, is sometimes packaged in bags as small as 1.5 kg. The amount of grout you will need depends on the tiles and the width of the joints—as a rough guide, you can expect to use about 1.2 kg of grout for each square metre of 200 by 200 mm tiles laid with 6 mm joints.

On many jobs, the only tools you need to install tiles are a box-notch trowel to apply mortar, a pointing trowel to pack in grout and a caulking gun to seal the space above expansion joints. If you plan to tile round a flagpole or anything else projecting from the concrete, you can lay mosaic tiles to follow the curves roughly, but you will have to pre-shape quarries with a tile nipper or a pair of heavy-duty pliers.

You may need to cut quarry tiles to make them exactly fit an existing concrete slab and avoid overlapping expansion joints, which must be left free to shift. Make a dry-run layout of two full rows of tiles at right angles along the edges of the slab. If the tiles fall short of or overlap an edge or expansion joint by less than 25 mm, adjust the spacing. If the shortage or overlap exceeds 25 mm, though, you should hire a heavy-duty tile cutter and cut tiles to fill in the empty space.

The Anatomy of Tile Paving

The structure of tile paving. Tiles are placed in mortar over an absolutely smooth concrete slab. The slab rests on firm, well-compacted soil—or a sub-base of crushed stone or hoggin if the soil is not firm—and slopes away from the nearest wall so water will flow off. The mortar bed is made of two layers: a skim-coat layer of cement slurry that bonds mortar to the slab, and a thicker mortar top coat that holds the tiles.

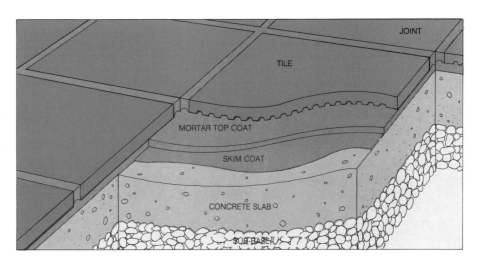

The Mortar Bed

1 Mixing the mortar. Prepare stiff mortar by mixing 1 part Portland cement to 3 parts soft sand and a minimum of water. You will need to use about 3 kg of Portland cement to prepare sufficient mortar to cover half a square metre. The mortar should be of a consistency thick enough to form peaks when you pull out the trowel. Set the mortar aside and prepare cement slurry for the skim coat by mixing cement with water to which you have added a bonding agent such as SBR. Add just enough water to make a fluid paste.

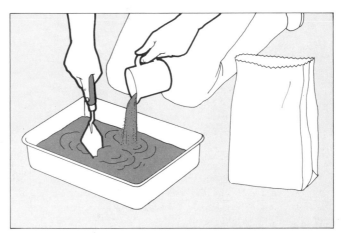

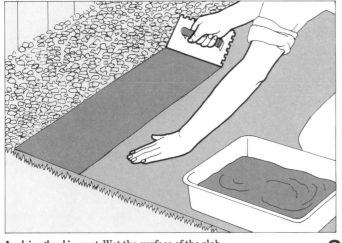

2 Applying the skim coat. Wet the surface of the slab with a broom soaked in water. Then spread cement slurry over the slab with the long, smooth edge of the trowel. Set the edge of the loaded blade where you want to begin the bed. Holding the trowel at a 45 degree angle while pressing down firmly, spread slurry paper-thin over an area ½ to 1 metre long and 300 mm wide.

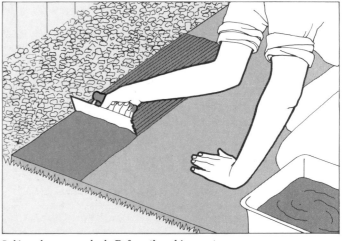

3 Raking the mortar bed. Before the skim coat hardens, scoop a trowelful of mortar on to the underside of the blade. Again using the smooth edge of the blade, spread a layer of mortar 20 mm thick over the skim coat. As soon as the skim coat is completely covered, use the long, notched edge of the trowel to rake lengthwise through the mortar, pressing down firmly against the surface of the concrete slab to form a bed of uniformly thick ridges.

Laying Quarry Tiles

1 **Seating the first tile.** Position the first tile, face up, at the corner, aligning the outside edges with the sides of the slab. Spread your hand over the tile's face, and push the tile downwards into the mortar bed to seat it. Tap the tile with the wooden handle of a trowel to force mortar up between the ridges on the underside of the tile.

2 **Laying adjacent tiles.** Leave uniform spaces for grout between the tiles as you proceed to seat and embed them. Lay tiles all the way across the mortar bed and then work in parallel, widthwise rows to cover all the mortar. Tiles made with projecting spacer lugs will automatically line up an equal distance apart when you abut the lugs. To space tiles lacking lugs, use a strip of wood between 6 and 9 mm wide (or of the width determined by your dry-run layout) as a gauge.

3 **Truing the tile bed.** To check that the tiles lie flat and even, place a long, straight board diagonally across the row after laying the first group of tiles. If necessary, flatten tiles by tapping the board gently with a hammer. Align the outside edges of the tiles while you can still shift them. Repeat Steps 1 to 3 across the edge of the slab, flattening and aligning each group of tiles as you go. Tile up to, but not over, expansion joints. Then work in parallel rows to the edge of the slab that is farthest from any building.

You can stop work at any time, but if you do, be sure to scrape excess mortar from the sides of the last tiles laid. When you have covered the entire concrete base, clean the area as described on page 37. Then let the mortar cure for at least 48 hours before you fill the joints with grout.

A Machine
for Straight Cuts

1 **Scoring the tile.** Set the guide on a quarry-tile cutter to the number of millimetres you want to remove from the tile. Lift the handle bar and place the tile, face up, against the guide. Lower the bar. Holding the tile steady, press down on the movable handle and push it smoothly away from you to score a straight line across the tile.

2 **Cutting the tile.** Place the tile in the clamp at the end of the cutter with the scored line centred under the clamp. Lower the handle bar, then tap it gently with the edge of your open hand. A clean, straight split will result.

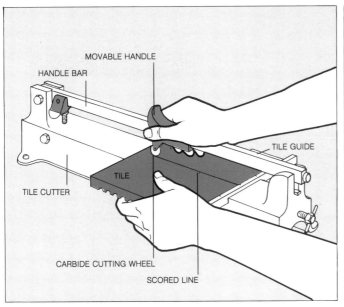

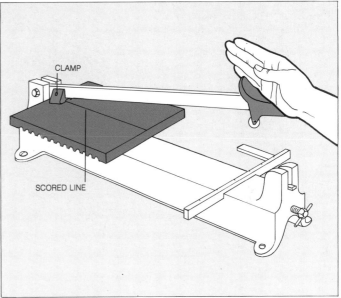

A Nipper for Curved Cuts

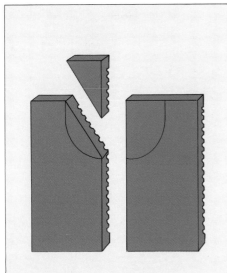

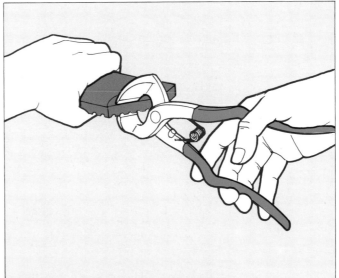

1 **Marking the curve.** If you have to install tile round a pipe or other round projection, make a cardboard template of the required cut and trace it on to the face of the tile. Use a quarry-tile cutter to remove most of the unwanted segment. If the curved area falls within a tile *(above)*, cut the tile in half, shape each and butt the halves.

2 **Making the cut.** Holding the tile firmly, use a tile nipper or heavy-duty pliers to break off small bits of the excess at a time. Do not expect curved cuts to be as perfect as straight ones. When you finish tiling, fill the space along the curve with mineral wool or foam strips and caulk so that irregularities will not be noticeable.

Laying Mosaic Tiles

Installing sheets of tiles. Mosaics come already assembled and evenly spaced on sheets of paper or fabric mesh so you can lay them by the sheet rather than individually. Start by spreading a large enough mortar bed at the corner of the concrete slab to hold one or two full sheets of tiles. Without removing the paper or fabric, seat the tiles at the corner—tile side up if the mosaics are back-mounted *(right)* and paper side up if they are face-mounted *(right, below)*. Following the instructions for laying quarry tiles, bed the mosaics and true them. The space between adjacent sheets should be as wide as the space between tiles on the sheet. Continue across the width of the slab, then in parallel rows. At expansion joints or the ends of rows, use a utility knife to cut sheets to fit. If you are using face-mounted tiles and the mounting paper is not the peel-off type, wet the paper with a sponge and lift it off before the mortar begins to set. With either kind of tile, let the mortar cure for 48 hours before grouting the joints.

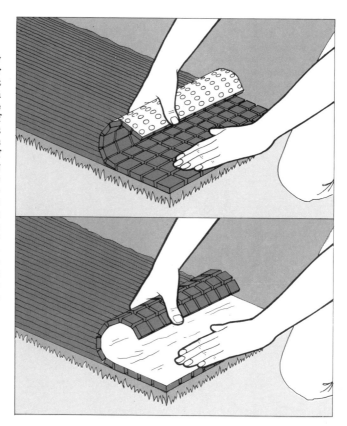

Three Ways to Fill Joints

ROLLED PAPER

1 Preparing the grout Pour water into a bucket; add a small quantity of ceramic tile grout mix, following the manufacturer's instructions. Stir until the grout is smooth and has the consistency of wet sand. If necessary, add water. Some grout must stand for 20 minutes and then be restirred before use; check the label.

2 Trowelling grout into joints. Stuff newspaper or tissue paper into the spaces above expansion joints or round curved-cut tiles, to keep these spaces clean. Start on the section of tiling nearest the building, making sure that the joints are completely clean. Slice a trowel full of grout on to the blade of a pointing trowel and set the top of the blade half way along one joint. Tip the trowel so the grout forms a mound in the joint. Make similar mounds, 75 or 100 mm apart, in as many joints as you can reach.

3 Levelling the grout joints. Spread the grout into the joints with a window-washing squeegee or a piece of stiff cardboard. Press hard enough to pack the grout and to force out air. As you work, push excess grout towards nearby joints.

4 Cleaning the joints and tiles. Sprinkle a generous amount of dry grout mix over the grouted joints and rub with dry hessian, using a circular motion. This action compacts the grout and prevents unsightly cavities that might appear as the grout dries and shrinks. Use the hessian dabbed with grout mix to scour the face of the tile. Then sweep the grout dust from the surface.

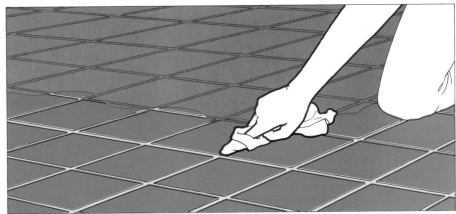

5 Edging with grout. To cover the exposed edges of the tiles and slab, use a pointing trowel to place a trowelful of grout on the exposed edge. Then, holding the blade against the top edge of the tiles at a 45 degree angle, run the tip of the trowel along the ground to spread the grout evenly. Cover the tilework with hessian and sprinkle it for at least three days to let the grout cure.

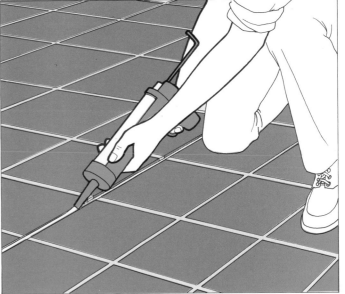

6 Filling expansion joints. After the grout is cured, remove the paper from the expansion joints and from round the curved-cut tiles. Then press into them a compressible material such as mineral wool or foam cut to fit the joints. Leave a gap of 10 to 15 mm above the filling material.

7 Sealing expansion joints. Use a caulking gun to fill the space above the filler with a self-levelling proprietary silicone or polysulfide caulk. Wipe any caulk that spatters on the tiles immediately, using the solvent recommended by the manufacturer. Let the caulk dry until it is not sticky before walking on the tiles.

The Rough-Hewn Appeal of Natural Stone

No masonry material is more handsome or durable than the oldest: rock. It is heavy to work with, but its very weight makes a structure that is solid in look and in fact. A flagstone path laid dry in sand—without mortar—resists being heaved by frost. And the simple dry stone walls that crisscross many parts of the countryside, standing after centuries of northern winters, are still a good model for low, home-built walls.

Even stone can shift if not mortared—a dry wall may require a bit of fixing each spring—and maintenance-free stone paving and walls should be laid with mortared joints in mortar beds over concrete bases. The mortar must be thick to prevent it from seeping out of the joints. To strengthen the bond between paving stone and mortar, cement slurry—a barely wet mixture of cement and water—must be placed under each stone.

With or without mortaring, the secret of handsome stonework is locking the irregular surfaces of the stones together snugly. How easy this part of the job turns out to be will depend on the form of stone you choose. Natural or quarried rubble produces the most rustic-looking walls; irregular flagging—also known as crazy paving—gives the most rough-hewn paths. Any of these forms require trial and error to arrange. The dressed and semi-dressed stones *(bottom, right)* that create gridded wall patterns and the rectangular flagstones that form geometric paving need less experimentation as you go along.

All three forms—rubble, dressed stone and flagging are produced from a variety of stone types, and which type you use depends largely on what is available from nearby quarries. Granites, which are usually greyish in colour, are the hardest and most durable, but also the most difficult to cut and highest in price. Limestones vary in colour and in degree of hardness, from very compact to granular. Slates, purple, grey and green, are hard and non-porous; because they are naturally stratified into layers, they are commonly split into flagging. Slate is, however, often expensive. Sandstones are available in many colours, from cream and pink to red; most are easy to cut and trim.

Since no two stones in nature are ever exactly alike, no two stones you buy will be identical in size, shape or colour. You can estimate quantity roughly, however, on the basis of the form of stone you want.

Flagging is sold by the square metre; to determine how much you need, measure the area you plan to pave and allow about 10 per cent extra for waste. Rubble and dressed and semi-dressed stones are also sold by the square metre. To determine how much you need, multiply the number of metres in the length of the wall you want by the height and add 10 per cent to allow for wastage.

Because of the irregularity of stone sizes and surfaces, accurately estimating the amount of mortar and cement slurry you will need to use is difficult. As a starting point, you can figure about 15 kg of Portland cement and 37 kg of sand for each square metre of paving, and 52 kg of Portland cement and 130 kg of sand for each cubic metre of wall.

Before delivery day, clear a large space close to the work site and spread out tarpaulins or plastic sheeting to protect the lawn. For moving large stones around, hire a trolley—it reduces the amount of lifting you must do. Standard masonry tools are used, and standard precautions are necessary: lift with your legs, not your back; wear heavy gloves; and put on goggles whenever you trim or split stone.

The Stones a Mason Works With

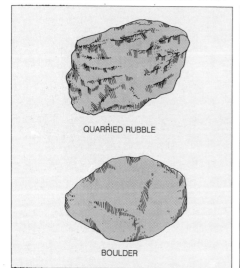

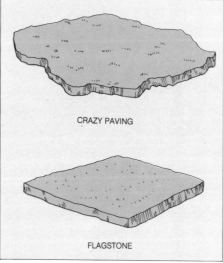

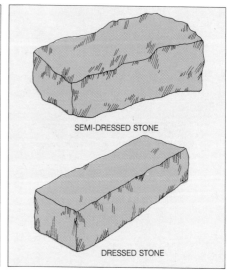

Rubble for a rustic look. Rubble is uncut stone, quarried as well as natural field and river stones. Most suppliers sell only quarried rubble, in pieces 150 to 450 mm in diameter. Quarried rubble's rough surface holds mortar better than the worn surfaces of boulders.

Flagstones for paving. Flagging is made by splitting stone in thin slabs. It may be laid as irregular crazy paving or cut into patterns. Flags range from ¼ to 1 square metre in area and from 10 to 50 mm in thickness. For a sand bed, flagging should be 35 to 50 mm thick; for a mortar bed, the flags should be 10 to 25 mm thick.

Dressed stone for an easy fit. Semi-dressed stone is roughly trimmed. More carefully and expensively shaped versions are termed dressed stone. Widths from 100 to 150 mm, heights from 50 to 200 mm, lengths from 250 mm to 1 metre are usually available.

Laying Flagstones on a Sand Base

1 **Fitting stones.** Stake the area you plan to cover with flagging, excavate it to a depth of 75 mm and lay down a 50 mm layer of sand, following the techniques on pages 78–80. Starting at one corner, arrange three or four 35 to 50 mm thick flags on the sand at a time. Line up the straight edges with the outside of the excavation and fit irregular edges together so that joint spaces will be 10 to 15 mm wide. Use a pencil to mark segments of stones to be trimmed for a snugger fit.

2 **Trimming small segments.** Place the stone on a bare section of the sand bed. Then, wearing goggles, knock off small unwanted pieces by hitting them outside the pencil marks with a bricklayer's or stonemason's hammer. Save the chips to use as fillers between large stones. If a segment is hard to remove, undercut it first by chipping off bits from the bottom edge.

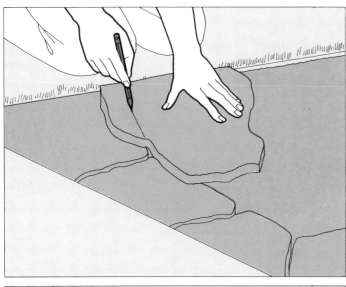

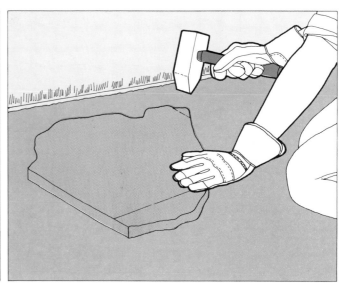

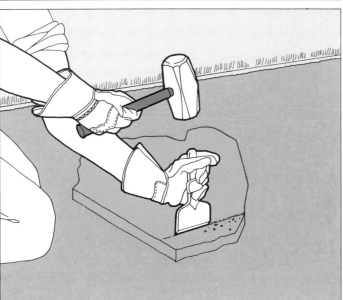

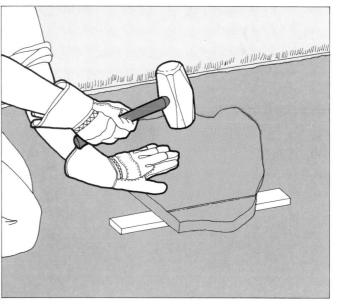

3 **Scoring large segments.** To remove a large segment of flagging, place the stone on sand and score along the drawn line with a bolster and a heavy hammer.

4 **Splitting off large segments.** Prop the scored flagging on a board with the unwanted segment tilted upwards beyond the edge. Tap the segment repeatedly with a hammer until it falls off. If the stone does not split readily with this treatment, score it along the sides and the back, then prop it up and tap it again.

5 **Bedding the stones.** Working from one corner of the paved area, tap each flag firmly down into the sand bed with a rubber mallet. The top of each stone should lie about 10 mm above ground.

6 **Truing the surface.** After bedding a row or two of flagging, set a spirit level on top of the stones to see if their surfaces are even. Put additional sand under stones that are too low, and scoop out sand from beneath high ones.

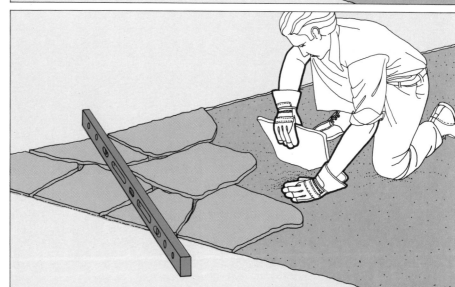

7 **Filling the joints.** Shovel additional sand over the flagging and sweep it across the stones until the joints are filled to the brim. Water the surface and let it dry. Repeat the process until the joints are filled with sand and compacted. To discourage any weeds, sprinkle herbicide into the joints.

Mortaring Flagstones on to a Concrete Base

1 Making a dry run. If you do not have an existing base, lay concrete, following the instructions for making an unreinforced slab of general-purpose concrete. Let it cure for one week. Arrange 10 to 25 mm thick dry stones on the base with no more than 20 mm spaces between them. Trim the stones as you go. Prepare a batch of stiff mortar by mixing 1 part Portland cement to 3 parts soft sand and a minimum of water—only enough to make the mortar hold the shape of a ball when you grasp it. In a separate container make cement slurry: Portland cement containing enough water to give it the consistency of thick cream. Then remove three or four stones and wet the concrete with a damp brush.

2 Bedding the stones. Trowel a 25 mm thick layer of mortar over the wetted area. Put back the stones and tap them down about 10 mm into the mortar with a rubber mallet. When you have embedded a dozen stones or so, use a level to check that they are flush.

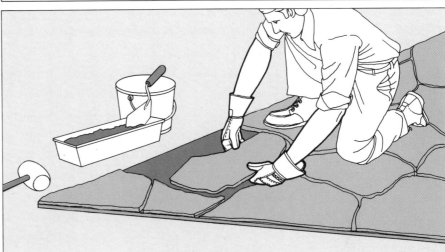

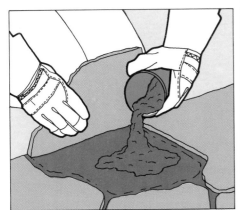

3 Applying cement slurry. Immediately after levelling the stones, pick up one flag at a time from the mortar bed and use a paper cup to dribble ¼ to ½ a cupful of cement slurry into the depression it leaves. Replace the stone and tap it back into position with a mallet. Recheck the level.

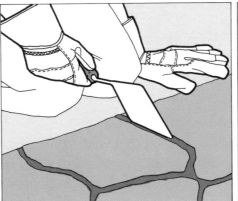

4 Filling the joints. Using the pointed end of a trowel, pack the mortar between the stones. Use a sponge to clean off excess mortar from the surface of the flagging. Let the mortar harden for an hour or two.

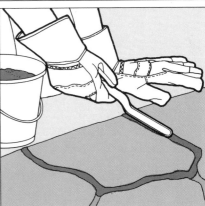

5 Finishing the joints. Use the top of a concave jointer, or a length of metal such as an old bucket handle, to recess the joints by a millimetre or two to help rainwater drain off the paving. Sponge off the mortar smears, and let the mortar cure for at least 24 hours before walking on the stone paving.

The Tricks of Building a Dry Stone Wall

You can still build traditional mortar-less stone walls by following the procedures practised over the centuries by generations of wallers. Dry stone walls need neither mortar nor concrete footings since the weight of the stones and their interlocking placement hold them together. If you have never built one before, it is best to limit yourself at first to a wall ½ to 1 metre thick and no more than 1 metre high.

You can use stones picked up from fields, but if they are too rounded, they may require considerable cutting to make shapes that join securely. Most builders buy quarried rubble, which has been squared off. Easily workable types—sandstone, limestone, shale or slate—are best.

A dry stone wall is built directly on the ground or, for better drainage, on a bed of sand. It has overlapping joints like a stretcher-bond brick wall. But it also has several unique features. One is the bonding stone, the first stone of the first course. Ideally it should be as long as the wall is thick, since it is placed crosswise to anchor the wall, tying the course at the front to the course at the back.

The front and back courses of stones do not make a solid wall. Small stones are used to balance the large ones, the space between the courses is filled with more small pieces, and gaps in the front and back are filled by hammering "chink" stones into them.

The faces and ends of a dry stone wall are not vertical but slope slightly inwards from a broad base, because each successive course is inset slightly from the one beneath. This taper can be judged by eye, or with a home-made device called a slope gauge (below, left).

Although the bulk of a dry wall contains no mortar, many builders lay mortar under a coping of broad flat stones. This mortared cap seals out water that may freeze and dislodge stones. You can also lay strong mortar inconspicuously in the core of the wall to give it added stability.

While building, observe a few rules that have been followed by craftsmen over the years: tilt stones downwards towards the centre so that the gravitational pull against the stones will compact the wall and help to keep it intact. When turning corners, avoid mitred joints—those with angular stones butted together at the ends. Never stack joints one above the other; always overlap. And do not be too meticulous; a rough wall generally looks better—and is sturdier—than a fussily even one.

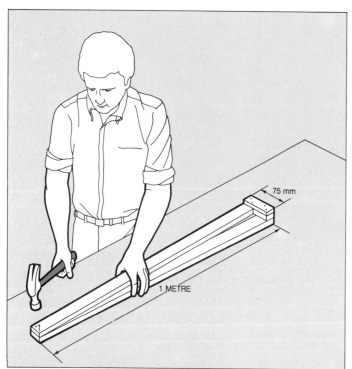

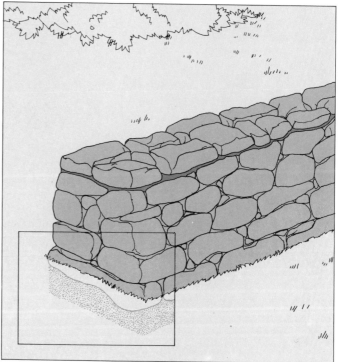

The slope gauge. Each end and face of a dry stone wall must taper inwards. To gauge this slope, nail together two lengths of wood at one end. Complete a right-angle triangle by nailing a short piece across the two lengths of wood and supporting one end with a small block to keep the long pieces flush. This short piece should measure 7.5 mm for each 100 mm of wall height.

The anatomy of a dry stone wall. A dry stone wall sits on a 125 mm layer of sand in a 150 mm trench. At the base is a bonding stone that goes from front to back and is overlapped by other stones. Unlike bricks or semi-dressed stones, which are laid flat, rubble pieces tilt towards the centre of the wall. As each new course is added, it is inset so the entire wall tapers slightly. The top layer of stones is mortared to seal out water.

A Wall for All Seasons

1 **Setting the bonding stone.** Dig a 150 mm trench the length and width of the wall, then fill it with about 125 mm of sand. Pick an even-faced stone that is as long as the wall is thick and place it at the end. This is your bonding stone—it helps hold the wall together. If you cannot find a long enough stone, make the bond with two stones.

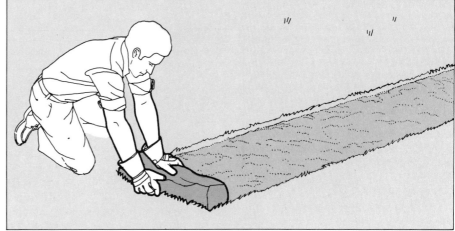

2 **The first course.** Lay stones along one side of the wall, then the other, alternating large and small stones, thick and thin ones, and placing long ones lengthwise, not across the wall's thickness. Lay each stone flat, never on its end or side, but set so that any slope of the upper surface angles downwards into the centre of the wall. Use the biggest stones for this first course, saving smaller ones for later—and the flattest ones for the top of the wall.

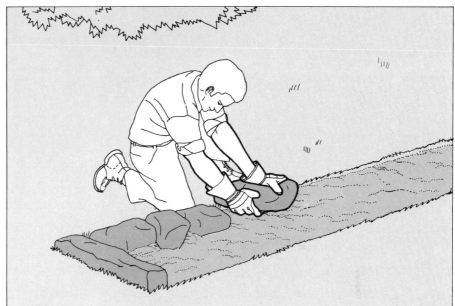

3 **Filling in the centre.** After you have laid 2½ to 3 metres on both sides of the first course, fill in the centre with small stones, building it up until the course is reasonably level.

4 **The second course.** Begin at the bonding stone and place on it an oblong stone with the length parallel to the wall; it will thus overlap the adjacent first course stone. Its top surface should angle slightly downwards towards the centre of the wall. Its outer edges should be slightly set in from the first course. To check this inset with a slope gauge *(right)*, use a level to keep one long side vertical; measure the slope with the other.

Continue laying second course stones along one side, then the other. Choose stones of a length that will overlap joints in the first course, of a shape to conform approximately to the surface underneath, and of a thickness to keep the top of the course approximately level. Check the slope each time. Then fill in the centre.

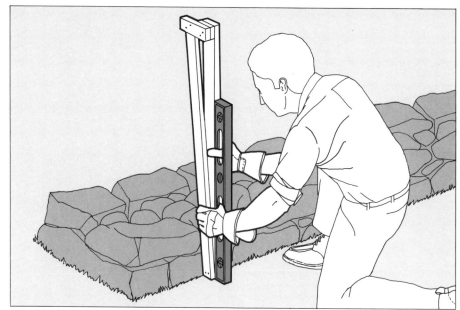

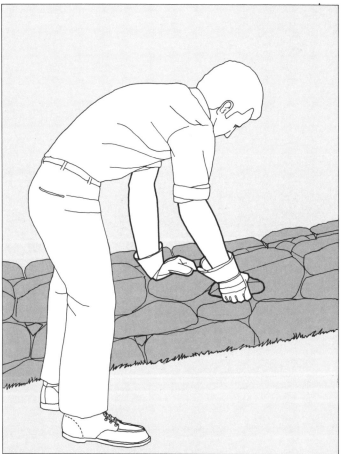

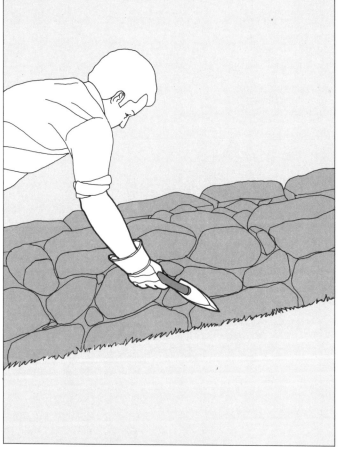

5 **Shimming.** The stones will not always seat firmly on those underneath. Angle the ends of each as you set it. Insert stone chips or small rocks as shims under the front or back edge until the stone rests securely and its weight tilts inwards.

6 **Chinking.** After two or three courses have been laid, fill gaps between stones by driving narrow stones in with your hammer. This chinking process locks the wall tight and helps keep weight pressing inwards from both sides. As you lay up the later courses, use the slope gauge to check the inset; judge the horizontal level by eye.

7 **Mortaring the final course.** If you want to apply a mortared cap, cover the next-to-last course with a 20 mm layer of mortar, following either of the recipes for strong mortar given on page 12. Then set in the stones you have been saving for the top. Fill in the gaps between these stones with mortar, building up the centre of the joint to prevent pockets where water might collect. Trim excess mortar from the sides.

Interlocking Stones for a Corner

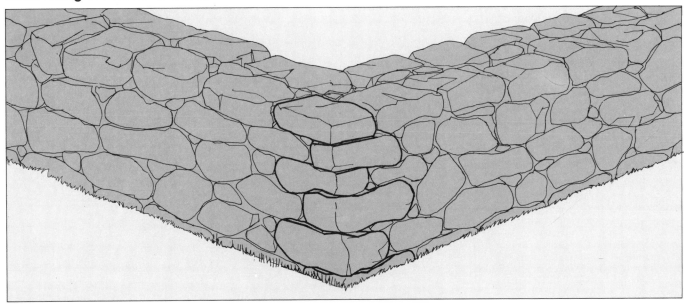

Intersecting the corner stones. Lay stones up to the corner as you would if you were building a straight wall. But at the corner, for the last stone in the first course of the inner face, use a large stone that will overlap the first inner course of the turn. Lay the outer first course the same way. In the second course, set the last stone short of the corner so that its end will meet the side of the first stone round the turn. Overlap succeeding courses in the same way.

The Wet Wall

If you want a wall that is more regular and more maintenance-free than a dry stone wall, use stones that are at least roughly rectangular, not rubble, and mortar them together over a concrete base. This "wet" construction is often used for retaining walls, which require weep holes and gravel fill to drain off water.

For a low wet wall—no more than a metre high—observe a few variations on the building techniques used for rubble walls. A footing is needed. An entire first course is laid down—this time with mortar surrounding each stone—and later courses are added with the stones overlapping the joints below like a stretcher-bond brick wall. Keep all stones level. And do not build as massively as with rubble; because mortar rather than the weight of the stones holds a wet wall together, it need be no more than half a metre wide.

To preserve the somewhat irregular contours of the stones, the final raking, or trimming, of the mortar joints is generally deeper than with bricks. Follow one of the recipes for strong mortar on page 12 and make sure that mortar beds are thick and fluffy. As soon as the mortar is trowelled on to the bed (or footing), it is ready for the stone; no furrowing is required.

Anatomy of a terrace wall. A low wall that is 400 mm wide sits on a 200 to 250 mm thick concrete footing. To lead away water from the soil behind it, a retaining wall must have weep holes at the bottom and gravel fill behind to enable water to seep down to the weep holes.

A Wall Bound by Concrete

1 **Laying the mortar bed.** Dig a trench for a concrete footing that will extend about 125 mm beyond the base of the finished wall on all of its sides and is deep enough to reach solid ground—200 to 250 mm is usually sufficient. For a terrace wall, dig out about 600 mm of earth behind the wall to allow for the gravel fill. Pour the footing and let it cure for at least 48 hours. Then put down a 20 mm thick layer of mortar on the slab, spreading only enough at a time to keep ahead of your stone setting. After throwing the bed, pat, but be careful not to compact, the mortar; it should still have a fluffy texture when you have finished.

2 Setting the bonding stones. Set into the mortar a bonding stone that stretches from front to back, centring it on the slab. Add stones along one side of the first course of the wall, leaving a 10 mm gap between stones for the mortar. Tap the stones down into the mortar, striking them with the handle of the trowel. If you find after placing a stone in position that you have made a mistake and must reset it, first wash off old mortar.

3 Filling the centre. After you have laid stones along both front and back sides of the first course, fill in the centre with odd stones—size and shape are not crucial—and cover each stone with mortar, adding more stones until the course is level. Throw mortar into the spaces between the outside stones. Then lay the sides—but not the centre—of the second course similarly, using a slope gauge to determine the correct inset.

4 Making weep holes. After laying, but not filling in, the second course, drive a broom handle into the wet mortar between stones of the first course. Push the stick through the wall. If it meets a centre rock, reach in and remove that piece so that the stick can continue, or pull out the stick and try another spot in the wall. When the stick has reached the other side, wiggle it a bit to make sure it has made a clean hole and pull it out. Repeat about every metre. Then fill in the second course and lay additional courses.

5 Raking the joints. Complete the wall by laying the flattest stones on top and mortaring them in as with the dry stone wall. Rake the joints between stones with a piece of wood, compacting and removing enough mortar for it not to be obtrusive. After the mortar has set for a day or so, fill in behind the wall with gravel to within 200 mm of the top. Then cover the gravel with topsoil.

Concrete Blocks for Economical Construction

Concrete blocks give the mason two major advantages: economy and speed. A block wall costs up to a third less than an equivalent brick wall and takes about half as long to build. The gain over natural stone is even greater.

There are two main types of concrete block. Dense concrete blocks are heavy and robust, and are intended to carry great loads. Lightweight concrete blocks, which are easier to handle, come in both load-bearing and non-load-bearing grades. Both types of blocks may be solid or cored and are available as either facing blocks, made in several different finishes and colours, or plain building blocks, some of which are not suitable for external work unless covered by rendering or facing masonry.

Concrete blocks come in varying sizes. Their thickness ranges from 75 to 215 mm. Typical face sizes are 440 by 215 mm and 390 by 190 mm. In Australia, typical sizes include 390 by 190 mm and 290 by 90 mm. There is also a wide selection of non-standard shapes and sizes for special purposes (below).

Blocks are laid like bricks. Both are anchored to a concrete footing with a furrowed mortar bed, but mortaring subsequent block courses differs slightly from brick technique, and some types require steel reinforcement. Also, mortar for dense blocks should be stiffer than for bricks; use a recipe for strong mortar on page 12.

The rules governing the height of brick walls apply equally to those constructed of concrete blocks. A block wall built with 100 mm thick blocks should not be higher than 600 mm; one built with 200 mm thick blocks can be twice that height.

Because block is economical, it is often used to make a core for what looks like a structure of stone or brick. A brick veneer can be mortared directly over a completed block structure. Or you can build up the block and the casing at the same time, anchoring the facing material to the blocks with wall ties. This method is particularly well suited to building a barbecue, for it leaves a cavity between the block and the sheath so that they can expand independently when the barbecue is used. Their expansion rates differ, and a bond between the two materials might cause breakage.

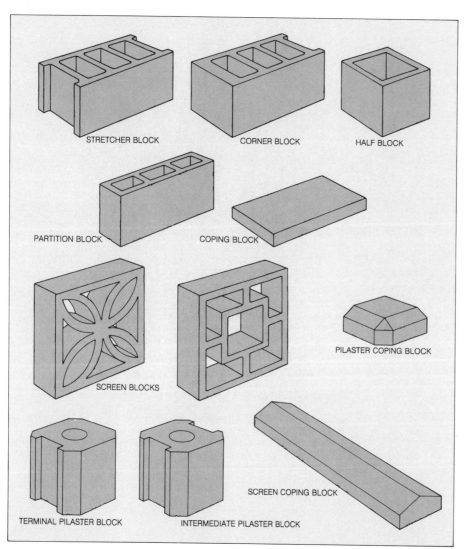

STRETCHER BLOCK

CORNER BLOCK

HALF BLOCK

PARTITION BLOCK

COPING BLOCK

SCREEN BLOCKS

PILASTER COPING BLOCK

TERMINAL PILASTER BLOCK

INTERMEDIATE PILASTER BLOCK

SCREEN COPING BLOCK

A Block for Every Spot

Choosing the right block. The stretcher block is the most common. It may have mortar-joint projections at both ends, and often incorporates two or three hollow cores separated by partitions called webs. A variation of the stretcher, called a corner block, is flat on one end for use where the end will be exposed. Partition and half blocks are handy shapes for tailoring a block core to fill a brick casing. Partition blocks can also be used to make weep holes to drain water from behind a retaining wall.

Where cores of blocks would be visible, coping units are often used in place of hollow ones or are laid on top of them. However, screen blocks, used for light and airy walls and partitions, have cores that are decorative and are meant to be seen. Pilaster blocks support screen walls and are recessed to allow screen blocks to slot into place. Pilaster blocks come in two forms—intermediate, for use along the length of a screen wall, and terminal, for use at each end. Coping blocks are available for capping such walls.

How to Lay Blocks

Mortaring blocks to each other. Stretch a mason's line between the leads of the wall—constructed like brick leads. Trowel a two block long mortar bed on to the tops of blocks so that 15 mm ridges of mortar cover the core webs as well as the edges of the blocks. Do not furrow mortar for ordinary blocks, although you may have to for solid or screen blocks. Stand two blocks on the ground and butter the mortar joint projections at one end of each. If the block has no mortar joint projections, simply butter one end of each block. Lift each buttered block by its webs, and in one motion push it into the mortar bed and against the adjacent block to make 10 mm joints. Trowel away oozed mortar.

Rainproofing a Block Wall

Filling the cores. To finish the top course of a cored block wall, use coping blocks, a coping of stone or brick, or fill the cores in the top course with mortar. A floor of metal mesh under the top-course block will keep the fill from dropping to the bottom of the wall. The mesh is metal lath cut with metal shears into strips two blocks long and about 10 mm wider than the cores. Throw a mortar bed for the top course and push the edges of the mesh strips into the mortar; then lay blocks on top. Finally, trowel mortar into the cores so the fill is even with the tops of the webs.

Attaching a coping. A course of coping blocks can be laid directly on to the top course of a wall built from either solid or cored blocks. For a stone coping over a wall laid with cored blocks, however, you must first fill the cores of the top course with mortar and then lay a 10 mm mortar bed. Set the coping on the mortar and fill in the joints as illustrated for a stone path. If you want the coping to slope, simply spread the mortar bed thicker along one side of the wall than the other.

A Decorative Screen Wall

1 Beginning the wall. Because screen blocks are laid in a stack bond pattern in which the vertical joints line up, a screen wall must be supported by reinforced pilasters at each end and at least every 3 metres along its length. Set out the footing, which should be twice the width of the pilasters and extend beyond each end of the wall by half that amount. Lay out a dry run of blocks and mark the centre point of each pilaster block with intersecting string lines. Pour the footing and embed 16 mm steel reinforcing rods at the marked points. The rods should be about 50 mm shorter than the final screen block. Secure the rods with guy ropes while the concrete cures overnight. Start the first pilaster by laying mortar round the base of a rod at one end of the wall.

2 Starting the pilasters. Lower a terminal pilaster block over the reinforcing rod, aligning it so that its recess points towards the centre of the wall. Tap it securely into position on the mortar bed. Pack mortar into the pilaster cavity (*right*) and check that the block is level. Lay pilaster blocks on top of each other with 10 mm, furrowed mortar joints, building up the pilaster to a height of three blocks, equivalent in height to two standard screen blocks. Begin the other pilasters in the same way, using intermediate pilaster blocks for pilasters which are part way along the wall. Allow the mortar to set overnight before laying the screen blocks.

3 Laying the screen blocks. Start the first course by laying a mortar bed 10 mm thick and two blocks long next to an end pilaster. Furrow the bed with the point of a trowel and then butter one side of a screen block. Slot the block into the recess in the pilaster, mortared side inwards, and press it down firmly into the mortar bed. Check that the block is level. Repeat this at the next pilaster and fill in the first course between the two leads as for brickwork; put the buttered edge of each block against the adjoining block and set it on a furrowed mortar bed. Butter both sides of the closure block and carefully set it in place. Repeat the procedure, working from pilaster to pilaster, until the first course is completed. Lay the second course in the same way, taking particular care to ensure that the continuous vertical joints between courses are perfectly aligned.

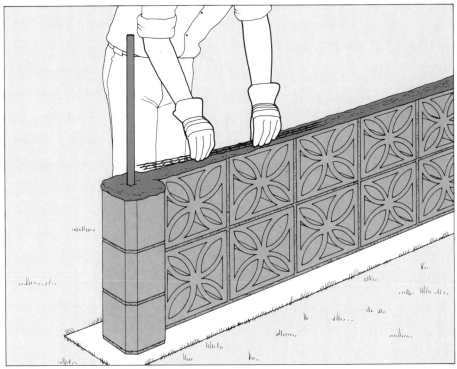

4 **Reinforcing the wall.** The mortar layer between the second and third block courses should be reinforced with special brickwork reinforcing mesh for extra strength. Use mesh about 50 mm narrower than the width of the wall, cut into lengths slightly shorter than the distance between the reinforcing rods. Lay a mortar bed between the first and second pilasters. Press a length of mesh into the mortar. Add three more pilaster blocks to the first pilaster, pressing the first block over the mesh to tie the screen blocks to the pilaster. Lay the third course between the first and second pilasters. Continue working from pilaster to pilaster until you have finished the third course. Add the fourth course as described in Step 3, opposite.

5 **Completing the wall.** Build the wall to a maximum height of 1.8 to 2 metres, reinforcing alternate courses with steel mesh. Complete the top of the wall by mortaring screen coping blocks over the screen blocks and pilaster coping blocks over the pilasters (*left*).

A Block Staircase

Masonry steps made of a block shell filled with sand and rubble are easier, quicker and less costly to build than poured concrete steps. Before you begin to build, plan the steps carefully, following the guidance on tread and riser dimensions on page 66. To simplify your work, choose blocks that co-ordinate with the dimensions of the steps. The risers should equal the height of a single block plus a 10 mm mortar joint, and the tread should be about two-thirds the length of a block.

The first stage in constructing such steps is to pour a 100 mm thick concrete slab for them to rest on. Make the slab 100 mm wider and 50 mm longer than the steps and landing. Slope the slab 2 mm for each 100 mm of length so that when finished the steps tilt slightly down from the house. They will then drain well and will be easier to climb. Make an expansion joint between the slab and the house foundation.

To improve the appearance of block and poured concrete steps, many home owners paint or veneer them. Masonry paint makes pores and mortar joints less prominent, and rendering hides them completely. Caution: only render the sides of the steps—rendering on the treads would crumble when the steps were used. A veneer of brick, tile or stone, however, is durable as well as decorative.

You can attach a masonry casing to existing steps or to ones you have built yourself. If the steps are already there, you will probably have to fit the material to them by trimming it and by widening or narrowing mortar joints. A casing also makes the first step higher than the others, a problem most easily solved by paving the path leading to the steps.

If you build steps like those shown here and on pages 66–67, you can solve the fitting problems in the planning stages. Start with a slab wide and long enough to support the veneer. Pour the slab below ground level to make the first step equal in height to the rest. You can also retain 10 mm mortar joints and eliminate most trimming if you tailor the tread depth of the steps to the casing material.

Building the Steps

1 Laying the side walls. After the concrete slab has cured for two to three days, outline the steps on the slab with a chalk line and steel square. Use solid blocks for the sides and front edges, so that no cores will be visible, and lighter, cored blocks elsewhere. Begin at the front edge with a solid block and use stretcher blocks to extend the first course, levelling each block as you lay it. If the blocks have mortar joint projections, end the course with a corner block. Start the second course with a solid block, leaving two-thirds of the block length for the tread of the first step. Complete one side wall this way, then the opposite one.

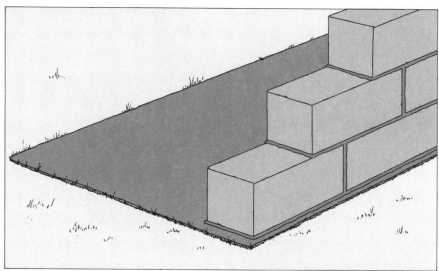

2 Filling in the treads. Stretch a guide line between the side walls and throw a one-block, furrowed mortar bed on to the slab. Butter the edges of a corner block or a cored block without mortar joint projections (not the cross webs in this case), turn the block on its side to hide the cores and lay it against the side wall. Complete the first tread, and after it has set for an hour, fill in the space behind with scrap masonry and sand. Tamp the fill so that it is level with the top of the first tread.

For the other treads, reposition the guide line, throw a mortar bed along the back third of the preceding tread, and repeat the first-tread procedure. Fill in the landing at the top with stretchers laid on their sides.

Sheathing Steps in Veneer

1 **Encasing side walls.** Butter the bricks and mortar them to the sides of the block core, following the treads and risers of the steps as closely as possible. The casing should extend far enough in front of each riser and above each tread and the landing so that the veneer material will align with the side wall casing. To achieve this fit with existing steps, adjust the thickness of the mortar joints or cut the casing material.

If you build steps that you plan to sheath with brick, like those illustrated, minimize cutting by making the tread depth 1½ brick lengths plus the dimensions of two mortar joints. Start the first course of the side casing with a half brick, positioned so that the next brick in that course will be even with the front of the block case. Lay four courses with the stretcher bond pattern, positioning each brick with a gauge rod and level. Start the next three courses 1½ bricks back from the first four. Step each successive three-course tier in this manner until the sheathing rises one brick higher than the landing.

2 **Paving the steps.** Mortar veneer to the first riser, using a guide line to keep the veneer flush with the projecting sides; make the top course level with the first tread of the core, cutting and adjusting as necessary. Then mortar veneer to the first tread, bringing the tread veneer flush with the riser veneer. Pave the remaining risers and treads in this manner, then cover the landing with bricks laid lengthwise.

Barbecues
of Blocks
and Bricks

Among the most practical and attractive applications of the technique of building with inexpensive blocks, then covering with handsome bricks, is a free-standing barbecue. The bigger and more elaborate the barbecue, the more time and money you will save. In the barbecue below, concrete blocks fill a space equivalent to 10 or 12 times as many relatively costly bricks.

The purpose of such masonry is to support a cooking grill, a fire grate and an ash pan. All three are available from garden or leisure centres, hardware shops and large department stores. The grill, made of nickel or chrome-plated steel, should be rigid enough not to sag under the weight of food, and heavy enough to resist being pushed out of position accidentally. The charcoal-supporting fire grates are usually made in small sections of heavy cast iron; you will probably need more than one. The ash pan can be anything from a specially built sheet-metal container to a disposable aluminium grill pan.

You can adapt the construction shown on the following pages to suit the sizes of available components or your special needs and tastes. Buy the hardware before you finalize your plans. To change the height of a fixed grill, simply add or subtract courses of brick from the bottom of the casing and adjust the height of the core. Or change the shape of the barbecue itself: lay out the first course of the casing in the shape you

want and plan a block core to fill the interior. You can then accommodate larger or smaller grills, increase or decrease the counter space, or build in a second grill.

The open space in the fire box below the ash pan can be modified to store charcoal or to serve as a warming oven. To do so, set into the front of the fire box a door with a flange to support bricks above it; then build courses of brick up the sides and across the top of the door as high as the ash pan, and cover the space with a 5 mm steel plate. The plate is set into a mortar joint round the fire box as the bricks are laid and used as a base for a shelf of bricks.

A more elaborate variation is an ash-removal and fire-stoking door with a vent to control the draft. Install the door in a brick facing that closes in the fire box to the top of the barbecue. As a final touch, you can use the rim of bricks round the

A Plan for a Permanent Barbecue

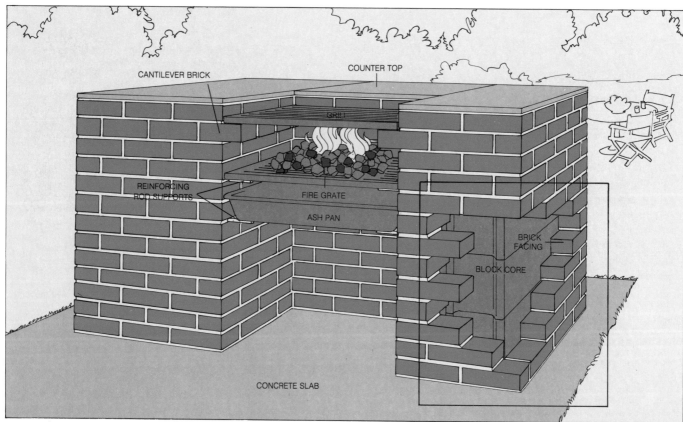

Anatomy of a barbecue. Beneath the brick skin of any block and brick barbecue lie courses of concrete block—in the barbecue shown here, one course of block for every three courses of brick—all resting on a 100 mm thick concrete slab. Twelve brick courses laid with 10 mm mortar joints will position the cooking grill about the same height as burners on a kitchen stove. The grill should be 150 mm to 250 mm above the fire grate. It is most attractively held by projecting cantilever bricks, while convenient supports for fire grate and ash pan are stubs of reinforcing rod fixed in mortar joints. These structural features, as well as the vertical dimensions, are common to most barbecues. The barbecue illustrated above measures 1.8 by 0.75 metres, and fits on a slab 2.1 metres wide and 1.5 metres deep. These horizontal dimensions can be varied to create other designs, and special conveniences—an oven or storage chamber—are easily added, as explained in the text above.

cooking grill to support a portable hood that converts the grill into a smoke oven.

Before building any barbecue, choose a site with care. The prevailing summer breezes should be your first consideration. If possible, locate the barbecue downwind from your house, your neighbour's house and the dining area. Orient the barbecue so that the wind blows smoke away from the cook and creates a draught for the fire. Before starting construction, check with your local building and fire authorities to see if local regulations affect your plan.

The construction job itself falls into two distinct stages: pouring a concrete slab *(pages 42–53)* and laying the bricks and blocks. Plan a slab large enough to provide a 150 mm skirt round the back and sides of the barbecue and a 600 mm apron in front for the cook to stand on. The slab should be 100 mm thick and made with general-purpose concrete. Allow the concrete to harden for a day or two, then lay the bricks and blocks. Finally, top the barbecue with a counter top of stone *(page 123)*, tiles or smooth concrete paving slabs.

To estimate material requirements, use a scale plan of the barbecue in conjunction with the basic shopping list on the right. The formulae given on page 84 will help you to work out the number of bricks and blocks and the volume of mortar you will need. Use the recipes on pages 12 and 26 to calculate how much Portland cement, sand, hydrated lime and coarse aggregate you must buy for the mortar and the concrete slab. Stone for the top of the barbecue should be ordered cut to size from a builders' merchant or quarry only after the bricks are laid; if stone is unavailable or too expensive, you can cut a working surface of tiles or paving slabs to size yourself.

A Basic Shopping List

For the slab:
Crushed stone or hoggin (if a sub-base is required)
Concrete

For the barbecue:
Concrete blocks (for the core)
Bricks (for the outer casing)
Mortar
Wall ties
8 or 9 mm thick reinforcing rod
Lightweight cardboard (from a stationer)
Stone, tiles or paving slabs (for the counter top)

Barbecue hardware:
Cooking grill
Fire grate
Ash pan

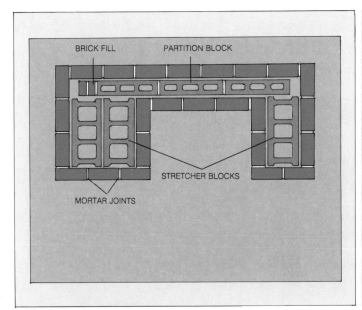

The pattern of bricks and blocks. Lay out the first course of brick in a dry run. Then fit a block core inside the brick, filling leftover spaces with bricks or trimmed blocks. The casing bricks are not mortared to the blocks or the individual block walls to each other; however, bricks used to fill out the core are mortared to the block wall they complete *(left in drawing above)*. Bricks are laid in the stretcher bond style, with staggered vertical joints, but the blocks can be laid directly on top of one another. For the basic barbecue above, the partition blocks at the back of the barbecue are laid in stretcher bond pattern, and two vertical bricks complete each course at alternate ends.

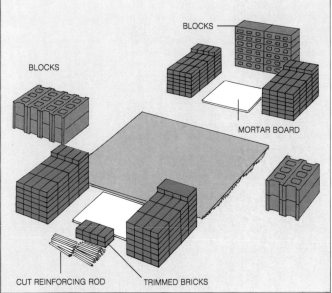

Setting up the work site. After the concrete slab is ready, save yourself hundreds of steps during the job by distributing bricks, blocks and mortar boards round the slab. Stack equal piles of bricks at the corners of the slab, about half a metre from where you will be working; between the stacks, place mortar boards. Position blocks near where they will be used. Before mixing mortar, trim blocks to fit the core if necessary. In addition, trim bricks to use as cantilever supports for the grill; and cut reinforcing rod to 200 mm lengths to support the fire grate and ash pan. The basic barbecue opposite calls for whole, untrimmed blocks, but it requires eight trimmed bricks for the grill and 32 cut pieces of rod for the grate and ash pan.

Putting Bricks and Blocks Together

1 **Starting the brick casing.** After a concrete slab has been poured and cured, use wall-building techniques to lay bricks. With a chalk line, mark a guideline for the back of the barbecue 150 mm from the edge of the slab. Using a steel square as a guide, chalk a second line 150 mm from one side of the slab, and build a stepped three-brick corner, or lead, at the intersection of the two lines. Extend the first course of bricks along the back of the barbecue to the far corner (in the basic barbecue shown here, lay five more bricks), then turn the corner at the other end, using the steel square again to make a true right angle. Construct a second three-brick lead at this corner, measuring carefully with a gauge rod.

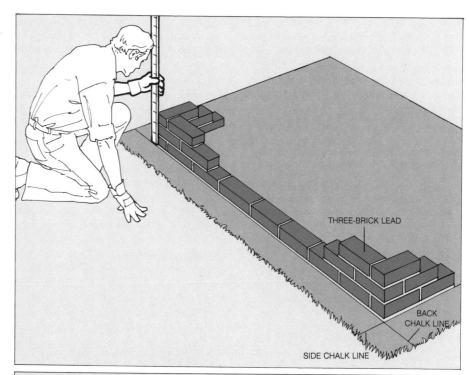

THREE-BRICK LEAD

BACK
CHALK LINE

SIDE CHALK LINE

2 **Starting the block core.** Complete the first course of brick all round the barbecue, then lay the second and third courses along the sides and back. This leaves a hollow space into which the blocks will be lowered. In the basic barbecue illustrated here, partition blocks form the back core and cored stretcher blocks fill the sides.

Trowel mortar on to the concrete slab, enough to make a bed for one block at a time. If you find that the mortar is so thin that it oozes out under the block's weight, sprinkle the bed with dry mortar to stiffen it. Space the blocks evenly inside the surrounding bricks without disturbing the bricks, leaving a 10 mm gap between bricks and blocks. Level the tops of the blocks with the top of the third brick course by adjusting the thickness of the mortar beds under the blocks. To fill a course of blocks at its end, you may have to mortar in a couple of up-ended bricks.

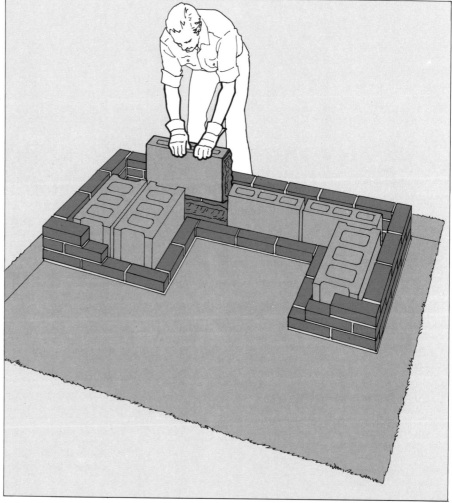

3 **Installing wall ties.** Complete the second and third courses of the brick casing, then lay wall ties across the gaps between blocks and bricks about every 250 mm, using diagonal ties at the corners. Throw the mortar bed for a three-brick lead at a rear corner of the barbecue, mortaring the wall ties in position as you proceed. When you come to a place for a tie, pick up the tie, lay the mortar, furrow the mortar with the trowel and push the tie into the mortar.

Repeat Steps 1 and 2. Install wall ties on every course of block. When you lay the bed for a new course of block, bend the ties out of the way, trowel on the mortar, then bend them back. Alternatively, lay the next course of bricks and blocks over the wall ties at the same time.

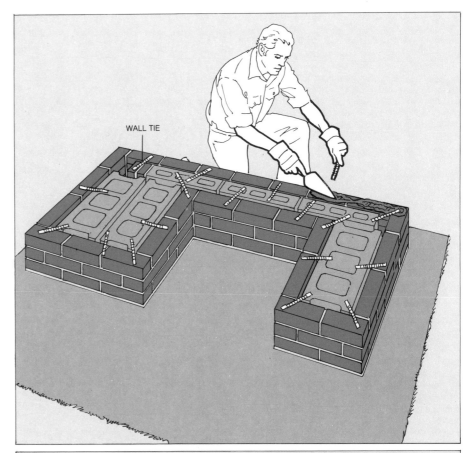

4 **Setting supports for the ash pan.** Lay blocks and bricks until the block core is three courses high, and the brick casing rises nine courses along the sides and back but only seven courses round the fire box. As you lay the eighth course of fire box brick, push 200 mm lengths of pre-cut reinforcing rod into the mortar bed on each side of the fire box. The rods should be evenly spaced and should project 100 mm from the casing. Lay the ninth course of bricks; then, in the mortar bed for the 10th course, set wall ties and reinforcing-rod supports for the fire grate.

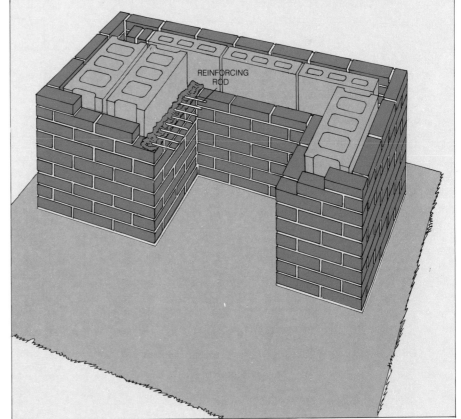

5 **Cantilevering bricks for the cooking grill.** As you lay the 12th course of brick, incorporate the trimmed bricks that will project, or cantilever, from the inner walls of the fire well, like brackets for a shelf, to support the cooking grill. Butter one side of each brick and lay it into the mortar bed so that the untrimmed end projects 100 mm. Set an up-ended brick on the inner edges of each of these bricks to keep them from toppling over while the mortar is setting.

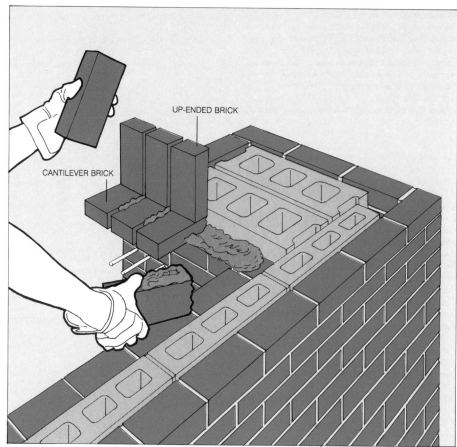

UP-ENDED BRICK

CANTILEVER BRICK

6 **Trimming the joints.** Let the mortar round the cantilevered bricks set for about 20 minutes. Then remove the up-ended bricks and, with a joint filler, trim excess mortar from the joints. Position the last set of wall ties and lay the 13th course of brick round the top of the barbecue.

7 **Paving over the blocks.** Fill in the space on top of the fourth course of block with a layer of brick in the pattern shown on the right. Lay a mortar bed on the blocks and butter these bricks on the ends and one side, so that the bricks are mortared to the block, the inner sides of the brick casing and the adjacent topping brick.

8 **Topping the barbecue with stone.** Lay a large piece of cardboard over one side of the barbecue top, weighting the cardboard with bricks to keep it from shifting. Mark the exposed side to identify it as the top and draw as much of the outline of the barbecue as you can on the underside. Remove the cardboard, complete the outline with a straightedge, then cut along the lines to make a template and set it on the barbecue. Trim the template for a close fit, and make similar templates for the other side and centre section. Trim 10 mm from each end of the centre template to allow for mortar joints in the stone top.

At a builders' merchants or quarry, have three pieces of stone cut to match the templates. Lay them with mortar on top of the barbecue, as shown in the instructions for a block wall. Let the mortar dry for two days, then coat the stone and its mortar joints with a proprietary resin-based stone-sealing compound to protect it against inevitable splatters of grease.

Picture Credits

The sources for the illustrations in this book are shown below. Credits for the pictures from left to right are separated by semi-colons, from top to bottom by dashes.

Cover: Ken Kay. 6: Ken Kay. 10,11: Martin Brigdale. 12 to 17: Drawings by Whitman Studio, Inc. 18: Drawings by Roger Metcalf. 19: Drawings by Jackson Day Designs. 20 to 25: Drawings by Nick Fasciano. 27 to 29: Drawings by Peter McGinn. 30: Drawing by Adolph E. Brotman – Drawing by Jackson Day Designs. 31: Drawings by Jackson Day Designs. 32, 33: Drawings by Adolph E. Brotman. 34,35: Drawings by Peter McGinn. 36: Drawings by Whitman Studio, Inc. 38: Courtesy of The Cement and Concrete Association, Slough, Bucks. 41: Drawing by Peter McGinn. 42 to 52: Drawings by Ray Skibinski. 53: Drawings by Ray Skibinski (2) – Drawing by Jackson Day Designs; Drawing by Ray Skibinski. 54: Drawings by Peter McGinn; Enrico Ferorelli. 55: Dan Budnik – Enrico Ferorelli; Drawings by Peter McGinn. 56: Courtesy of Portland Cement Association. 57: Courtesy of Portland Cement Association (2) – S.W. Newbury, Courtesy of Concrete Construction, Addison, Illinois (2). 58 to 61: Drawings by Peter McGinn. 62: Drawings by Jackson Day Designs. 63: Drawings by Roger Essley/Adisai Hemintranout. 64: Drawings by Jackson Day Designs. 65: Drawings by Ray Skibinski. 66, 67: Drawings by Adolph E. Brotman. 68 to 71: Drawings by Nick Fasciano. 72: Wolf von dem Bussche. 74: Drawings by Peter McGinn. 75: Drawings by Peter McGinn – Ken Kay. 76, 77: Drawings by Peter McGinn. 78 to 80: Drawings by Nick Fasciano. 81: Drawings by Jackson Day Designs – Drawings by Nick Fasciano. 82 to 93: Drawings by Nick Fasciano. 94, 95: Drawings by Jackson Day Designs. 97 to 101: Drawings by Ray Skibinski. 102 to 111: Drawings by Nick Fasciano. 112: Drawings by Whitman Studio, Inc., except bottom right by Jackson Day Designs. 113: Drawings by Whitman Studio, Inc. 114: Drawing by Whitman Studio, Inc. – Drawings by Jackson Day Designs. 115: Drawings by Jackson Day Designs. 116, 117: Drawings by Whitman Studio, Inc. 118 to 123: Drawings by Ed Vebell.

Acknowledgements

The editors would like to extend special thanks to Susie Bicknell, Paris; Emily Brandt-Clarke and Iki Mann, Hamburg, and Elizabeth Hodgson, Sydney. They also wish to thank the following: Autoclaved Aerated Products Association Ltd., Birmingham; Beton de Paris, Paris; Brick Development Association, Windsor, Berks; Brick Development Research Institute, Melbourne; British Ceramic Research Association Ltd., Stoke-on-Trent, Staffs; Buck and Ryan Ltd., London; Cement and Concrete Association, Slough, Bucks; Cement and Concrete Association of Australia, Sydney; Centre Scientifique et Technique du Batiment, Paris; Fédération des Fabricants de Tuiles et de Briques de France, Paris; Frisch-u. Transportbeton Lübeck GmbH, Lübeck; H.C. Hill Ltd., London; Hire Service Shops Ltd., Reigate, Surrey; Instarmac Ltd., Minworth, West Midlands; Le Lycée Téchnique du Batiment Saint Lambert, Paris; Martinsen GmbH & Co., Ratzeburg; Ogden Yorkstone Ltd., Bradford, Yorks; Dr. L.L. Pearson, Slough, Berks; Max Schön, Lübeck; Sika SA, Paris; Stone Federation, London.

Index/Glossary

Metric Conversion Chart

Approximate equivalents—length

Millimetres to inches		Inches to millimetres	
1	1/32	1/32	1
2	1/16	1/16	2
3	1/8	1/8	3
4	5/32	3/16	5
5	3/16	1/4	6
6	1/4	5/16	8
7	9/32	3/8	10
8	5/16	7/16	11
9	11/32	1/2	13
10 (1cm)	3/8	9/16	14
11	7/16	5/8	16
12	15/32	11/16	17
13	1/2	3/4	19
14	9/16	13/16	21
15	19/32	7/8	22
16	5/8	15/16	24
17	11/16	1	25
18	23/32	2	51
19	3/4	3	76
20	25/32	4	102
25	1	5	127
30	1 3/16	6	152
40	1 9/16	7	178
50	1 15/16	8	203
60	2 3/8	9	229
70	2 3/4	10	254
80	3 1/8	11	279
90	3 9/16	12 (1ft)	305
100	3 15/16	13	330
200	7 7/8	14	356
300	11 13/16	15	381
400	15 3/4	16	406
500	19 11/16	17	432
600	23 5/8	18	457
700	27 9/16	19	483
800	31 1/2	20	508
900	35 7/16	24 (2ft)	610
1000 (1m)	39 3/8		

Metres to feet/inches		Yards to metres	
		1	0.914
2	6' 7"	2	1.83
3	9' 10"	3	2.74
4	13' 1"	4	3.65
5	16' 5"	5	4.57
6	19' 8"	6	5.49
7	23' 0"	7	6.40
8	26' 3"	8	7.32
9	29' 6"	9	8.23
10	32' 10"	10	9.14
20	65' 7"	20	18.29
50	164' 0"	50	45.72
100	328' 7"	100	91.44

Conversion factors

Length

1 millimetre (mm)	= 0.0394 in
1 centimetre (cm)/10 mm	= 0.3937 in
1 metre/100 cm	= 39.37 in/3.281 ft/1.094 yd
1 kilometre (km)/1000 metres	= 1093.6 yd/0.6214 mile
1 inch (in)	= 25.4 mm/2.54 cm
1 foot (ft)/12 in	= 304.8 mm/30.48 cm/0.3048 metre
1 yard (yd)/3 ft	= 914.4 mm/91.44 cm/0.9144 metre
1 mile/1760 yd	= 1609.344 metres/1.609 km

Area

1 square centimetre (sq cm)/100 square millimetres (sq mm)	= 0.155 sq in
1 square metre (sq metre)/10,000 sq cm	= 10.764 sq ft/1.196 sq yd
1 are/100 sq metres	= 119.60 sq yd/0.0247 acre
1 hectare (ha)/100 ares	= 2.471 acres/0.00386 sq mile
1 square inch (sq in)	= 645.16 sq mm/6.4516 sq cm
1 square foot (sq ft)/144 sq in	= 929.03 sq cm
1 square yard (sq yd)/9 sq ft	= 8361.3 sq cm/0.8361 sq metre
1 acre/4840 sq yd	= 4046.9 sq metres/0.4047 ha
1 square mile/640 acres	= 259 ha/2.59 sq km

Volume

1 cubic centimetre (cu cm)/1000 cubic millimetres (cu mm)	= 0.0610 cu in
1 cubic decimetre (cu dm)/1000 cu cm	= 61.024 cu in/0.0353 cu ft
1 cubic metre/1000 cu dm	= 35.3146 cu ft/1.308 cu yd
1 cu cm	= 1 millilitre (ml)
1 cu dm	= 1 litre see **Capacity**
1 cubic inch (cu in)	= 16.3871 cu cm
1 cubic foot (cu ft)/1728 cu in	= 28.3168 cu cm/0.0283 cu metre
1 cubic yard (cu yd)/27 cu ft	= 0.7646 cu metre

Capacity

1 litre	= 1.7598 pt/0.8799 qt/0.22 gal
1 pint (pt)	= 0.568 litre
1 quart (qt)	= 1.137 litres
1 gallon (gal)	= 4.546 litres

Weight

1 gram (g)	= 0.035 oz
1 kilogram (kg)/1000 g	= 2.20 lb/35.2 oz
1 tonne/1000 kg	= 2204.6 lb/0.9842 ton
1 ounce (oz)	= 28.35 g
1 pound (lb)	= 0.4536 kg
1 ton	= 1016 kg

Pressure

1 gram per square metre (g/metre^2)	= 0.0292 oz/sq yd
1 gram per square centimetre (g/cm^2)	= 0.226 oz/sq in
1 kilogram per square centimetre (kg/cm^2)	= 14.226 lb/sq in
1 kilogram per square metre (kg/metre^2)	= 0.205 lb/sq ft
1 pound per square foot (lb/ft^2)	= 4.882 kg/metre^2
1 pound per square inch (lb/in^2)	= 703.07 kg/metre^2
1 ounce per square yard (oz/yd^2)	= 33.91 g/metre^2
1 ounce per square foot (oz/ft^2)	= 305.15 g/metre^2

Temperature

To convert °F to °C, subtract 32, then divide by 9 and multiply by 5	
To convert °C to °F, divide by 5 and multiply by 9, then add 32	

Typesetting by Tradespools Ltd., Somerset, England
Printed and bound by Artes Gráficas Toledo, S.A., Spain
D. L. TO: 1681 -1984